CRYING IN THE LINEN CUPBOARD
and Laughing in the Sluice

CRYING
IN THE
LINEN
CUPBOARD

- and Laughing in the Sluice -

Trials and triumphs of
trainee nurses in the 1950s

Margaret Morris

UNITED WRITERS
Cornwall

UNITED WRITERS PUBLICATIONS LTD
Ailsa, Castle Gate, Penzance, Cornwall.
www.unitedwriters.co.uk

British Library Cataloguing in Publication Data:
A catalogue record for this book is
available from the British Library.

ISBN 9781852001735

Printed and bound in Great Britain by
United Writers Publications Ltd.,
Cornwall.

'Nurses. They make the best wives in the world, until you feel ill – and then God help you!'

Quote from Alan Morris

Chapter One

She stood on the edge of the pavement, a suitcase at her feet, and looked hard at the house on the other side of the road. A tall young woman, not particularly pretty, nor indeed plain, but like most people, somewhere between the two. At eighteen years of age and with the bloom of youth about her, a relatively slim figure, and a liveliness of expression showing on her face, she was attractive enough to warrant a second glance.

The house that was consuming her interest she must have seen dozens, no hundreds, of times before, as she got on and off the bus here during her recent schooldays; seen but not registered as anything special, as indeed it was not – just one of half a dozen large, three-storeyed houses built at the turn of the century, when Victoria sat firmly on the throne and Britannia ruled the waves. Number 2 Albert Terrace, even the name had royal connotations. The end of a terrace of six, one could see at the side of the house a double gateway leading to what might once have been stabling for a horse and carriage, as these were houses built for professional gentlemen, or successful trades people who could afford to bring wife and ever burgeoning family out of the squalor and smells of the town centre and move here to the suburbs where the air was fresher, and the adjacent municipal park provided perambulation for the latest twigs on the family tree and their attendant nursemaids.

Yes, definitely a house that had boasted domestic servants. The small third storey windows that seemed to be peering out from under the gutters, no doubt fronted maids' quarters. Rooms that were swelteringly hot in summer and freezing cold in winter.

On this late October day in 1948, with dusk already darkening the sky, lights burned in the two curtained bay windows of this unremarkable house. A house that had become special to the tall young woman regarding it so intently. Special, because this was where she was going to live for the next few weeks. Where she would have her bed and her possessions, where she would come 'home' to each evening, though of course, her real home was still with her mum and dad and little brother. Now that she had 'left home', a much anticipated event, this was where she would come to rest each evening.

Enough, enough, of this hesitation, and seizing her suitcase, she crossed the road, rehearsing as she went what she would say when the door opened.

"My name is. . . and I've come to. . ."

"Good evening. I was asked to report here. I'm. . ."

"Hello. I'm a new. . . I've come to start. . ."

School days behind her, it had been a long summer of helping in the house and garden. The church youth club (boys!), Saturday night hops in the village hall (boys!) and occasional visits to one of the dozen or so cinemas that flourished in the nearby town (sometimes boys). She had seen her contemporaries, one by one, packing their trunks and departing for further education. Now at last, her turn had arrived. Only nine years old when war broke out, the present shortages and austerity of post-war Britain were, to her, the norm, with memories of the time before the war hazy in the extreme. The euphoria of victory had passed and though the constant anxiety of loved ones away in the war zone had gone, as had the possibility of death raining from the skies, life in post-war Britain was tough. Rationing of food and clothing still bit hard and those items not officially rationed, were difficult to find. The country was poor, shabby and struggling. Boys still disappeared to do their National Service and came home grown into men and looking for employment. And employment there was – lots of it. The new Labour Government elected to establish the brave new world, the 'sunny uplands' promised by Winston Churchill, was turning out social legislation at a bewildering rate, and there included promise of new universities. Meanwhile, those places available were reserved, rightly, for men returning from war service and wanting to start or continue their interrupted careers.

But tomorrow, "Tomorrow will be a great day" as the popular song said. The National Health Service was going to look after everyone from 'the cradle to the grave' and everything it could offer would be FREE. Beveridge's dream? Or that of Aneurin Bevan?

Across the road, a low wall separated the pavement from a small flagged area in front of the house on which sat a lonely bush in a tub. No gate of course, that had gone with the ornamental railings from the top of the wall, regular blobs of metal being the only footprints remaining; gone to feed the hungry maw of the armament factories. An impressive front door in need of a coat of paint. A gleaming knocker and bell push. She knocked. It had begun.

The door was opened immediately by a stout middle-aged woman in an outfit that might have better graced a young and curvaceous Lyons Tea Room waitress. A frilly cream lace apron strained over a rounded 'tummy'. Matching lace sat on greying over-permed hair and a heavily made up face grinned a welcome.

"Good evening, my name is Margery Harvey and I have come to start my nurse training." There, it was said!

Still silent, the maid indicated by a twitch of her head that Margery should enter, whereby she disappeared into the house interior leaving Margery standing in the hall. It smelt of floor polish, energetically applied to both the floor and the staircase rising ahead. Two closed doors faced each other. From behind one, marked 'Common Room', came sounds of chatter interspersed with laughter, the other remained silent.

What to do? Margery hesitated. Go through the 'chatty' door? Knock and walk in? Try the other door? Follow the maid? – or just wait.

The problem was solved by the arrival of a brisk young woman, possibly in her mid-twenties, with a clipboard in her hand. "Ah! You must be Margery Harvey – you're the last." The newcomer couldn't have been more different from the lumpen maid who had answered the door. A nursing sister in navy blue dress, white apron, collar and cuffs and discreetly frilled cap. Twinkling blue eyes regarded her through upswept spectacles.

She was the last! "Oh dear, am I late?" Margery wondered if

she had misread her letter which had instructed 'Report by 5pm'. It must now be about 4.45pm, she thought.

"Not at all," came the reply. "Some of the nurses have travelled quite a long way and bus and train timetables don't always match our requirements. A couple have been here since 2pm! I think the best thing will be if you take your case up to your room, it's – the clipboard was consulted – "it's on the first landing; don't unpack, come down straight away and meet the others," and the sister gave a quick nod to the door opposite.

Picking up her case, Margery started up the stairs. One, two, three steps, the heavy case had to be manoeuvred, four steps and the end of it caught the banister supports and there was a loud crack.

"Can you manage, Nurse?" came a voice from the hall below.

Concentrating on guiding the large case up the narrow stairway, Margery didn't reply.

The voice came again, this time with an element of irritation. "I *said*, can you manage, Nurse?"

With a start Margery realised it was she who was being addressed. As Nurse! Belatedly she replied, "Yes, yes, thank you."

"Yes, thank you, *Sister!*" this time there was definitely a touch of frost in the tone. . .

Oh, Lordy, Lordy – not in the house five minutes and she had broken the banister and been less than polite to this sister, who was probably a Very Important Person. It was with relief that Margery reached the landing.

Yes, on the first floor, a square of white card on the door announced N Harvey and N McCall. Well, they'd got that wrong. . . she was M Harvey and presumably N McCall was her room mate. She wondered what "N" stood for. Nancy? Nora? Natalie? Nicola? She pushed open the door and gave a gasp of pleasure.

The room was charming. Modern furniture of some light wood. Pink curtains against white walls, matched the two bedspreads and two pink mats lay on shiny dark blue linoleum. This was infinitely more attractive than her bedroom at home with its dark furniture and faded carpet. N McCall had claimed the bed nearest the door, a pyjama case in the shape of a woolly dog sat on the pillow, so Margery heaved the suitcase onto the second bed and took a closer look around. Two chairs upholstered in dark blue, one large wardrobe and two dressing tables. In the corner a wash hand basin gleamed. Wow! Nancy, Nora, Natalie had arranged her possessions on one dressing table – a rather battered brush and comb set, a jar of Pond's vanishing cream and one of Snowfire hand cream. Feeling guilty, but unable to curb her curiosity, Margery picked up a small framed photo. It was of a middle-aged couple leaning on a gate of what could be a muddy farmyard. Yes, the white blobs in the background must be hens and these were N McCall's parents she supposed. Father sporting a cloth cap, worn so habitually that it appeared to have grown naturally out of his scalp. A collarless shirt and braces held up thick breeches that ended in boots. He looked, Margery imagined, anxious to get back. To what? His cows maybe. Mother, on the other hand, looked embarrassed at being photographed in her working clothes. She too wore boots, and a wraparound floral apron.

This really wasn't on, Margery reprimanded herself; examining someone else's possessions in their absence, so she grabbed her handbag and made her way downstairs. She was relieved to see that the banister supports all looked OK – so she perhaps hadn't done too much damage on the way up. Arriving in the hall she took a deep breath and opened the door marked 'Common Room'.

At first glance the room seemed stuffed with young women. They sat on a settee and in armchairs, on window seating running inside the bay window; were perched on arms of chairs, and anywhere they could find a space. A momentary hiatus in the level of chattering as all eyes swung to appraise the newcomer, then their interest was almost immediately squashed and conversations resumed, the noise rising again.

Thankfully, Margery spotted an upright chair only a yard or so inside the room and slid into it, trying to look as inconspicuous as possible. Everyone seemed to have someone to talk to. Were they all demonstrating to the rest their social competency in this new and unfamiliar situation, Margery wondered. Appearing to be at ease when, in fact, their every nerve was attuned to register the various aspects of this new life, as indeed were her own. She looked around. At the far side of the room a table was laid for a meal. In the centre were two large sliced loaves still in their wax

11

wrappers, but no other food was in evidence. The table cloth, so white and stiffly starched, it seemed loathe to hang downwards in places. The sideboard against which she was sitting caught her eye. On the top was a collection of glass jam jars, some holding about three inches of sugar, others a cube of what looked like butter. How very peculiar. Margery was pondering this oddity when a voice intruded.

"Hello, I'm Audrey Renton. And who are you?"

A plump dark girl in a red floral dress was making herself known.

"Margery Harvey – Hello."

"You've come far?"

"No, not really. My parents live in Buckshaw – that's about five miles from here. You?"

"Mine are in Garson, but I've come from Manchester today. Been nursing at Mary's for the last two years," Audrey went on.

Puzzling. Was she supposed to know who Mary was? But explanation followed.

"You'll have heard of St. Mary's Hospital for Women." This was a statement, not a question. "Obs and Gynae, you know."

Margery didn't, but thought it best just to nod wisely. What came as a surprise to her was that this girl had been nursing for *two years*. It had never occurred to her that some of her fellow students would not be as inexperienced as herself. That they wouldn't all have come from school or from other jobs in offices or shops. But Audrey Renton was continuing:

"My ward just admitted lists. Mainly repairs, hysts, a few Gilliams and of course, D & C's. Dozens of those!" She grinned.

This was a new and quite impenetrable language to Margery. This girl looked about the same age as herself, and was here for training, but was familiar with the language and work of a hospital. Nursing – as what? She spoke of 'my ward' as if she had been the queen bee. Margery was on the point of telling Audrey of her recent studies in anatomy and physiology (after all, one had to keep one's end up with whatever one had) when Audrey interrupted:

"I think someone over there is trying to catch your attention."

Across the room two of Margery's ex-school mates were waving and making 'come over here' gestures. Of course: Jane Kirkham and Doreen Melling, two girls familiar to her, but with whom she could not recall ever having had a conversation, were inviting her to join them. To see Jane Kirkham was quite a surprise. Margery had no idea that she aspired to a career in nursing, nor indeed that she had anything in common, or was friendly with the petite and dainty Doreen Melling. But there they were, drawn together in the face of a dozen or so strangers by a thread of familiarity, and inviting her to join them. Margery thought not, at the moment. Making her way across the crowded room was somewhat daunting, and she really had no wish to set up a sub-branch of the Grammar School Old Girls' Society, so she mouthed back "see you later."

So, Doreen Melling had made it at last. . . Everybody knew, couldn't possibly avoid knowing, that Doreen was GOING TO BE A NURSE. Joining the St John's Ambulance Brigade at the youngest possible age, she had appeared at school, as often as the rules would allow, in her uniform, her arm growing increasingly heavy with badges won for this and that. Later she could be seen at weekends trotting in the wake of stout and be-tweeded ladies with flairs on their hats, and permitted to hold bandages and make tea in the Brigade's first aid tent.

Latterly, of course, as someone rising eighteen years she had actually helped staff the tent, putting arms in slings, treating fainting fits and twisted ankles. Now, at last, the day had come to start training and she was pop-eyed with excitement.

The sixth form of a girls' grammar school in 1948 might be said to exist to produce teachers. Of course, a few pupils entered other professions, but in the main girls took variations of a higher school certificate and went off to training college or university and thence back to school on the opposite side of the classroom than had been their erstwhile position. A degree in an academic subject was considered sufficient to earn you a teaching post in a grammar school – knowledge of the theory and practice of education an added and unnecessary extra. Some girls went to domestic science college and into what later became known as the 'caring professions' but it was teaching that the headmistress and her staff really understood. Largely single ladies (after all, before 1939 local authorities would not employ married women) this was the path they had trodden themselves, that they understood and encouraged.

13

A lot lower on the list of possible employment for girls came nursing. The teaching staff knew that this was an honourable and very necessary profession for women, held in high regard by the general public, but felt they had spent seven years driving academic subjects into the girls only to have them seek training for work that required no stringent entry qualifications, was ill-paid and required long hours of menial labour. Still, this year the profession had gained three 'hopefuls' from one grammar school alone. Maybe more from elsewhere.

Meanwhile, Audrey Renton seemed to have found an audience elsewhere and Margery began to wish she had joined the two across the room, when the door opened to admit the sister whom she had met earlier. Conversation died and a couple of girls, more familiar with hospital etiquette, immediately stood up respectfully, hastily followed by the rest of the company.

With a gesture indicating 'sit', the sister, her hands now tucked into her apron bib, smiled round at everyone. "For those of us that haven't already met, I am Sister Lumsden and I'm the tutor in charge of the PTS – Preliminary Training School – that's you!" "My room, if any of you want to find me, is just across the hall. I hope you have all been getting to know each other, and as supper has now arrived from the hospital, I suggest we continue that process by eating together. After supper I will be wanting to see your NI and medical cards and to collect your ration books. We also need, if we are to live in harmony together, to discuss house rules and I will give you some idea of what will be happening tomorrow – and find you all a uniform. Right? Now if you will all take your sugar and butter rations from the sideboard we will eat."

So, that was what the jars were – of course! "Sister," – a small 'mousey' girl, had a question, "my boyfriend's coming for me at 7.30. Will we be done by then?"

"No, we will not, you are required here this evening, so I'm afraid he will be disappointed. Nurse Knight, isn't it?" Sister's tone brooked no argument and Nurse Knight subsided, looking rebellious.

A shuffling for position round the table, the chair at the end by unspoken consent left for Sister Lumsden. A bit like school dinners really, Margery thought, anticipating really thick butter

14

plastered on her bread. It seemed like forever since she had really *tasted* butter, her mother having scraped it on and scraped it off again in her efforts to make the family rations last the week. It would mean dry bread later, of course. So what?

The maid, her name it seemed was Anne, shuffled in with bowls of salad, a huge teapot and a pile of plates each holding three slices of what was known as luncheon meat. Bright pink in colour, with white flecks, this was the British austerity version of the delicious Spam that had come from America at one point during the war. Spam had been meaty and moreish but memories had faded and now luncheon meat must suffice.

Chatter ebbed and flowed. Jane Kirkham and Doreen Melling were ensconced one either side of Sister Lumsden, and at the other end of the table the disgruntled Nicola Knight was regaling Audrey Renton with the amazing virtues of her boyfriend whose name was Arthur. The elongated 'A's of Cumberland came across loud and clear: A-a-arthur worked on the m-a-a-rket in Kendal, he couldn't afford a c-a-a-r but had bought a motorbike on which to travel to see her – and now that bloomin' sister was stopping him. Margery had a feeling they were going to hear a lot about Arthur in the near future.

She really must identify her room mate, she thought, so put a general question to those around her. "I'm sharing a room with N. McCall, which of you is. . ?

"And that will be myself," a thin, dark haired girl answered. "Nurse Harvey? I'm Theresa McCall."

Theresa! That was a shock – "I had thought your name began with 'N'." General laughter had Margery blushing.

Sister Lumsden, having caught the drift of the conversation, explained, " 'N' stands for nurse. Christian names are for families and close friends on social occasions. You have now joined a profession and titles – nurse, sister, doctor and so on – are expected to be used." She nodded and resumed conversation with her neighbours.

"Now dares a ting – I'm to call mi friends 'Norse'!" Theresa's Irish voice indicated quite clearly where she called home, and if the strained look about her eyes was anything to go by, she felt a long way from those emerald shores and in a company a lot stranger to her than it was to Margery.

Theresa pushed her luncheon meat round her plate and finally

15

left it, only enjoying the bread and butter, the latter disappearing in its entirety.

Anne returned with the sweet; blancmange and jelly, soon polished off, crockery cleared, and sister asked that they be back in the common room by 7pm.

Unpacking a few of her things, Margery laid out black stockings and shoes for the morning whilst Theresa sat on her bed and bounced up and down a little, rolling out questions. At last Margery was the knowledgeable one. When did they get more butter? How far away was the hospital? Where would she get a ration book and medical card? Where was the nearest church? After this last question, a possibility seemed to occur to Theresa. "You *are* Catholic, aren't you?" she enquired.

Margery, rummaging in her handbag, answered, "No, Methodist."

This was greeted with silence. Then: "That's protestant, isn't it?"

"Um yes, I suppose so – why?"

"I've never spoken with a proddie before, and now I'm sleeping with one!"

"We really are quite normal, you know." Margery laughed. "Does it matter? Come on, *Nurse* McCall, let's go and hear words of wisdom from Sister Lumsden." And gathering up their bits and bobs they trundled downstairs.

Sister Lumsden, in spite of her 'in charge' manner, had screwed herself up for this day. Only the second school she had tutored, she enjoyed the company of the students and teaching was OK if she was allowed to do it in her own way, which in many respects she was not. A new school was always a challenge. Students came from many backgrounds, had varying ambitions, not always with abilities to match them. To get to know them was as exhausting as serving a ward full of patients. She already had a feeling that that Nurse Knight was going to be difficult. The starry-eyed idealists (was Nurse Melling one, she was certainly showing the signs) would fade away in the face of long gruelling hours. She would have to be specially aware of those who, having left elementary school at 14, had no experience of sitting through a lecture, of taking notes, of private study and, of course, of exams, either written or oral. Goodness knows, the theoretical knowledge needed by a nurse was pretty low in the league table of academic achievements, but still assumed great significance to those who had, hopefully, the intelligence but no experience of formal studying.

If only she had some input into selecting students, she thought. There were some, probably some in this present lot, who she would definitely reject. But there. This was a medium sized provincial hospital, Merton Royal Infirmary, without the famous name of the London training schools or even the size and reputation of neighbouring city schools. These could pick and choose from amongst many candidates. So, while the work force that staffed the wards consisted mainly of student nurses, a body of such must be maintained and there just were not enough girls coming forward, willing to work long hours for poor pay, for anyone to be too stringent in making a selection. The profession had relied too long on that body of dedicated spinsters left behind by two world wars – who was to follow them? Perhaps this great and glorious National Health Service, now suffering its birth pangs, would solve this and every other problem.

In spite of her own career doubts, Sister Lumsden was convinced that she and her senior tutor, the redoubtable Miss Bailey-Scott, plus all the visiting consultants and heads of departments could deliver as good a training as larger and more famous schools of nursing.

She had less than half an hour to do another quick read through of the students' applications and histories. The sooner she put names to faces and understood where they were coming from the better. Her notes were jotted down for this her first session, really as a check list of all that she must remember to tell them. She looked sadly at the bales of uniform dresses and aprons dumped in her room for want of an alternative place. All second-hand, some probably third and fourth hand. Sister Lumsden gave them a desultory kick. They were going to be a sad disappointment to their wearers.

Gathered in the common room, ration books and so forth accumulated in neat piles, the students, as expected, stood as the sister entered. She bade them sit and herself perched on the arm of the settee. Where to begin? First of all, she pointed out, all those under 21 years of age were, in law, minors, and as such, the hospital in the persons of matron and her senior staff, were 'in loco parentis' and had responsibility for their safety and wellbeing. To this end the house would be locked at 10.30pm

17

each evening and they were expected by then to sign the book in the hall to say that they were 'in'. If they wished to spend all night elsewhere prior to their day off, they must leave a note of their address.

"Welcome to Stalag 21. Heil Hitler." Anne Manning, a plump blonde girl with merry blue eyes who was already establishing herself at the clown of the group, whispered audibly.

Sister Lumsden smiled fleetingly, and added, "You may invite visitors into this room as you wish. Tea and milk are provided in the kitchen but meals, except for breakfast, will be taken at the hospital. Tonight was an exception for your arrival.

"Now 'Domestics'. This is a large house and it has to be kept clean. By You. Each morning you will be woken by Anne at 6.30am and between then and 7.45am, when breakfast is brought over, you will, along with your room-mate, undertake domestic tasks. A list is on the notice board."

This information produced glum looks, as it dawned on the girls that the shine on the floors and the brass bits and pieces, to name the obvious, would have to be maintained by their effort. Doreen Melling, the solitary hours of an only child behind her, thought it might be quite fun – all working together, her rosy vision of the life of a nurse so ingrained that it could even encompass before breakfast cleaning chores.

"And tomorrow," Sister Lumsden consulted her check list. "Tomorrow you will all report to Home Sister at the hospital at 9am and she will see that you find your way to the school. The hospital is about 20 minutes walk from here, or there is a bus which takes as long, fare 3d. I am sure there are some amongst us who know the way." She nodded at Doreen Melling and Jane Kirkham.

"Now your uniforms." The whole room perked up. "Please realise that these dresses are a temporary measure whilst you are in the PTS, you will have made-to-measure uniforms later. Meanwhile we should be able to find something to fit in these bundles. They will need ironing, which I am sure you can manage. The ironing room is on the top floor." She was unwrapping the dresses and holding them up to gauge the sizes. They had once been royal blue but were now varying shades of grey-blue due to frequent laundering and were shapeless, though each had been carefully mended where necessary.

Luckily Anne Manning incorrigibly saw the comic side and started to recite, "It was Christmas day in the workhouse. . ." then "Let my indescribably sexy body (size 18) get into one of those and I shall be a goddess – irresistible."

Margery was worried that none of these dresses would be long enough to cover her knees, she had trouble buying clothes even from shops carrying a reasonable stock and always looked first to see if there was a hem she could let down. She found one dress good and long but faded almost to grey. How many bodies had worn this before her, she wondered. Another, shorter but bluer would also be OK. Now, for aprons. Two each. One size to fit (or not fit) all. Only to be worn when doing housework or when visiting wards. She trundled off to be first to find the iron – 'student nurses for the use of'.

Sister Lumsden bid the company goodnight and left, duty done. She had hardly left the room when Nicky Knight erupted into the street to seek Arthur and his trusty bike. It was now 9.30pm. Would he still be waiting? The street was empty. Nicky stamped off crossly and flung her uniform across her bed. Sometime during the night it fell off and lay in a heap on the floor. She went to bed disgruntled and irritated by the whole evening which she saw as wasted.

Without the courage or the enterprise to knock and ask for his lady love, Arthur had got fed up and gone home.

The run home blew his irritation away. An open road, little traffic, the wind in his face and the throbbing roaring engine between his thighs, what more could anyone want. Tomorrow he would tune the engine slightly and wait for Nicky to contact him before making the trip again. Having a girlfriend working a distance away had given him the impetus to put a down-payment on the bike, and it engrossed him. He had to work extra overtime to meet the payments but it was worth the effort – in fact, he thought, if he had to choose between the bike and the girl, the bike would win – and the money spent on petrol would be saved. He would have to think about that. He pushed the bike into his mother's shed and gave the seat an affectionate pat. After all, a goodnight kiss with his girl would be OK, but with a bike? That would be silly. He locked the shed and went in to bed.

The house began to settle. Michaela Green was bothered. This wasn't what she had expected at all. The only child of scholarly parents, Michaela had done nothing at school, dreaming her way through till she was old enough to leave and get a job. And a variety of jobs she had taken, then abandoned, enjoying with friends an aimless existence of earning and then spending. Her parents had approved her sudden desire to be a nurse. At least it was a career, of sorts, not what they would have wished, but better than this mindless drifting, so they encouraged her, with misgivings as to her ability to cope with the pressures it would bring. Michaela saw herself clad in immaculate blue and white, drifting down a ward full of clean and very grateful patients, dedicated to her work and admired for her compassion, skill and wise understanding. Somewhere in the background there were handsome doctors in white coats saying things like, "I know that you can save him, if anyone can." Their dependence on her patience and skill leading inevitably to a closer relationship. She had read all the 'Sue Barton' novels from *Student Nurse* to *Superintendent Nurse*; had gobbled up Monica Dickens' *One Pair of Feet* and seen the film version three times. Her difficulty now was the gap that existed between this idealistic picture, tinged as it was with a good helping of 'Medical mystique' and the present: All this cleaning! Exploitation surely of those capable of higher things. The use of titles she approved. Significant people deserved the recognition of their calling. Of course she would expect to perform humble tasks at the beginning – a measure of her dedication, a trial which she would endure with composure and fortitude. Yes, she would just have to endure the domestic work for the sake of her chosen profession. She settled in her chair, the fascination of the medical world restored and anxious to meet what was to come on the morrow.

Theresa McCall couldn't understand why she felt so tired. She had been working long hours in a Dublin Geriatric hospital until yesterday; yet today, when she had been sitting down for most of the time, she felt whacked. It had been a long day, full of new experiences, sights, sounds. "Oh Lord – that pink stuff they had served for supper. Yuck!" Even going to bed would be a new experience. From what she could see one got onto a bed with a sprung mattress, not into it as she did with the feather one at home, that had curled round her with blissful touch. In theory since her two older sisters had left home she had had a bed to herself, but in practice during the night a small sibling had usually

20

crept in with her, seeking the warmth and comfort of her presence.

Undressing slowly, Theresa allowed herself the indulgence of considering the past twenty-four hours. It had started early at 5am when Paddy Murphy had come with his pony and cart to take her to the dockside. She wouldn't dwell on saying goodbye to her parents, lest a whisper of homesickness intruded. Theresa was the fourth of their children that her parents had seen off to new worlds. The eldest son, Patrick, was still at home helping Dad with the farm; one daughter, thankfully, was married and living in Dublin. She had two little ones who visited and gladdened their grandparents' lives. With three children now in America, that still left eight of them at home, but with the youngest, little Michael, now nearly six years of age, surely, surely baby-making days were over.

Theresa had boarded the Irish steamer and deliberately avoided several of her fellow countrymen who had stood out on deck watching Ireland disappear into the awakening day, and storing up the memory, some with tears running down their cheeks, to comfort them on any 'down days' that were to come.

Then there was the train journey to Merton and the disappointment that there were no Murphy sisters to meet her. The Murphy twins were the reason why she had come to Merton. A little older than herself, they had been neighbours and playmates at home and they had promised that one or both of them would be at the station to meet her.

Theresa had known a moment of panic at their absence, but thinking that they had been held up she had tried to buy a cup of tea at the station buffet only to have her coins refused as 'foreign'.

Standing forlornly at the station entrance, a kindly porter had found her a taxi, and, still worrying about having the wrong kind of money, she had been driven across town to Albert Terrace. She needn't have worried as the taxi driver waived away the proffered fare with a "Forget it, luv, you're going to be a nurse and I've a sympathy for the likes, I was on me way home anyway."

Altogether quite a day. A message had been waiting for her that just said, "Couldn't come, off duty change, see you tomorrow. Love Maeve and Maureen," so that explained that.

Theresa found her rosary beads and knelt at her bedside as she

21

had done every night of her life, and began her prayers. Half way through, her room mate Margery came to bed, and seeing the kneeling girl, stepped quietly over her protruding feet to reach her own bed. Theresa climbed into bed, exploring with her feet the cool, stiff cotton sheets, so unlike her mother's flannelette ones that had grown rough and knobbly with frequent washing.

"You're the nearest," a muffled voice came from the other bed. "The nearest to the light switch, switch it off, there's a love."

Electricity, Theresa thought as she climbed back to bed, was all very well, but a candle at your bedside only needed a puff.

Drifting off to sleep it occurred to her that today was Sunday, and for the first time in her life it had passed without her attendance at Mass. Something for confession – when she'd found the church, found a priest, found out what 'off duty' she could expect. Tomorrow. She slept.

Chapter Two

Jane was up and half-dressed when Anne started her journey round each bedroom to make her 'wake-up' calls. Doors were flung open with a crash: "Half-past six, Nurse," and click, on went the light. Early mornings were nothing new to Jane; her father ran a small but flourishing newsagents and tobacconist shop only a few hundred yards from the hospital gate. Jane had spent some part of the summer since she left school filling in for missing paper boys and delivering morning papers to the surrounding streets.

Early mornings were new to her room mate Doreen Melling, who had expected to be woken gently by her mother, who had the dining room warm and breakfast ready and waiting on the table. Nevertheless she jumped out of bed keen to get started on this new life so anxiously awaited.

Upstairs things were not going so well. Nicky Knight groaned, covered her head with the bedclothes and remained immobile. Her room mate Eileen Downy – a sensible, matter-of-fact young woman a little older than the rest – after several exhortations to "Get up – lazy cow," resorted to not-too-gentle prods, and eventually pulled the bed clothes off the recumbent Nicky, to howls of protest.

Eileen Downy began to think she had drawn a short straw in being roomed with Nicky. . . A hard-working girl, she had been employed at a residential home for blind children, a job she loved, when she was called home to nurse her mother through a serious illness. Mum recovered, and the need to earn money had driven Eileen to a local factory where she had met a young man just out of his apprenticeship and preparing to do his National Service. They were now engaged; Kevin was in the army in Germany and Eileen had embarked on nurse training with some trepidation at the thought of studying – "book-work" she called it, something that was foreign to her and indeed to her parents. Dad a builder's labourer, and Mum an office cleaner, they lived in a council house and had brought up their three children in a loving home, encouraging them to work hard and play as hard as funds allowed.

They were proud that all three of their kids were 'bettering themselves', with both Eileen's brothers undertaking trade apprenticeships, so that soon they would have a trained plumber, an electrician and perhaps a qualified nurse making their contributions to the world in general.

Eileen carefully removed her engagement ring and threaded it on a piece of tape to wear round her neck whilst in uniform, gave a final yell at Nicky sitting grumpily on the bed edge and began cleaning the bathrooms – the appointed task for the morning.

Meanwhile Jane Kirkham had started on their chores – dusting and hoovering the common room, cleaning out and re-laying the coal fire and laying the table for breakfast. Within a few minutes her room mate, Doreen, joined her and stood contemplating the ashes of yesterday's fire. Seizing a coal rake taken from the empty coal hod, she scraped vigorously at the grate sending up a cloud of ash onto Jane's newly dusted mantelshelf. Jane was not pleased and dusted it again.

Carefully Doreen lifted the half-burnt lumps of coal onto the hearth as she'd seen her father do on Saturdays and Sundays when the cleaning lady didn't come in. Next her problem was how to remove the ash pan. An unwieldy shape, and brimful, it had to be carried safely across the hall presumably to an ash bin in the yard. An idea struck. She would empty the ash into the coal hod and thus carry it more easily. Again a cloud of ash decorated the mantelshelf, again Jane dusted it and Doreen staggered out with the full hod and was directed to the appropriate bin outside. Tipping it in, the cloud of ash this time fell on herself, her clean apron, her hair and her face. Back in the house Anne supplied her with paper and wood and she managed to lay the fire, with advice from Jane, putting the half-burnt pieces of coal on top of the wood.

Jane was now emptying ashtrays and hoovering prior to laying the breakfast table feeling safe that no more ash would erupt. Doreen tidied the hearth, and regarded her handiwork. There was something missing. Of course, coal! Where did she get coal? Anne enlightened her, directing her to the cellar, obligingly turning on a dim electric light. Stone steps led down into a stygian black hole, the only glimmer of light, once she'd left the stairs, coming from a grating through which a street lamp outside shone eerily onto a gleaming heap of coal – and a shovel. Shovelling coal in a cold dark cellar before breakfast was something Doreen had never, in her wildest fantasies, considered would be part of nurse training, but if that was what was required, she'd have a go.

Getting the now very heavy coal hod up the cellar steps, one step at a time, was physically very daunting, but she made it. Tomorrow she would look at the fire with more appreciation and tomorrow too, *she* would do the dusting and table-laying. Fair's fair.

Eileen cleaned two of the bathrooms then sought her recalcitrant room mate. By now the house was alive with blue clad figures, cleaning, polishing, bustling about, intent on rendering the already clean house even cleaner – all except Nicky who, still in her dressing gown was sleepily ironing her uniform dress. Eileen informed her that two thirds of the allocated work was completed, the rest was up to her, so would she please GET A MOVE ON. She then returned back to their room to start her daily letter to Kevin and tried to let Nicky's ineptitude cease to annoy her.

Dear Kevin, Well, I've arrived and so far. . .

Breakfast was rather a giddy affair, sausages, bread and marmalade. Sister Lumsden did not put in an appearance which accounted for the noise and general relaxation as the company prepared to make the journey to the hospital. The letter sent to each one of them, accepting their application to train, had asked each individual to supply themselves with black, flat, rubber-heeled shoes, black stockings and if possible a navy blue coat for the journey between hostel and hospital. It was quite evident that some had found the latter request impossible as several of the

b

nurses sported coloured coats, loath probably to spend precious clothing coupons on something as mundane as a navy-blue gabardine. Margery, buttoned tightly into an ex-naval officers' great coat, was warm and snug. Her mum had spotted a small ad offering these 'war surplus' garments for sale *free of coupons*! She'd removed the crested buttons and replaced them with Bakelite ones – flower-shaped – that she'd cut off and saved from a pre-war coat of her own. The result was hardly high-fashion, but served a purpose. Topped with a variety of headscarves, woolly hats, berets and pixie-hoods a bedraggled and far from uniform company set off for the hospital.

Michaela, Audrey, Jane and of course Nicky, as one might have guessed, opted for the bus, the rest, with Doreen prominent as guide, set off to walk.

First the local postman, pushing his bike with empty bag back to the sorting office, greeted them with, "Morning girls. You the new lot? Best of luck to you." Lorry drivers, recognising them as nurses presumably by their black stockings, whistled and gave them the thumbs up, and when a delivery driver unloading bundles of newspapers, asked with a wink and a grin if anyone had time to give him a quick massage in the back of his van, Doreen didn't know whether to be offended or amused. All this badinage was received in good part by those familiar with the general reaction of the male sex to nurses in black stockings and they arrived at the nurses home as the others were alighting from the bus.

Home Sister's office at Royal Merton hospital was easily-found. A square space, like a large vestibule just inside the door, marked the division between the hospital proper on the left and the nurses' home on the right. A corridor ahead led into the interior. They were bidden by Home Sister to "Wait here and Clarry will come down and take you up to the school." And so, self-consciously, they stood around and did just that. Night staff, caps and aprons removed, appeared often in bedroom slippers to collect mail from the pigeon holes outside Home Sister's office. An enclosed phone box was well-used and a succession of non-residential staff who had 'normal' 9 to 5 jobs – physiotherapists, radiographers, laboratory workers, came and shed their coats in the cloakroom provided, donning white dresses, caps, overalls or tabards according to their individual discipline. Office girls tweaked their curls in the mirror provided – the life of the hospital was beginning another day – all avidly observed by the new student nurses.

By 9.05am the comings and goings had ceased and the aforementioned Clarry appeared. All eyes focused on the small personage framed in the doorway. Dressed in the regulation maid's red and white striped dress, a mobcap on her head, Clarry stood about 4 feet 6 inches tall and was almost as wide. A small rotund, individual as interested in appraising the new students as they were fascinated by her surprising appearance. "Follow me," she commanded, and feeling like giants, they all trooped after her. "Coats," she ordered, as they reached a row of recessed hooks, and they all, silent in this strange situation, continued to follow Clarry up the stairs. Progress was slow as Clarry had, like a child, to take one step at a time, her short legs lifted sideways and her hand clutching the banister which was level with her ears.

At the top a door marked 'Library' was flung open and Clarry stood back importantly as the nurses began to file in. It was at this point that a loud voice interceded. A high-pitched querulous voice calling, "Clarry, Clarry."

The effect was electric, Clarry spun round, replying, "Coming, Miss Bailey-Scott," and scurried off down the corridor towards the source of the summons.

The girls continued into the library, stood around the central table they found there and stared at each other. It wasn't quite clear who was the first one to giggle, but soon they were all rocking with half-silent laughter. "S-shush, or someone will hear," Eileen Downey tried to quell the rising hysterical mirth. "It's wrong to laugh at an affliction, that is, a handi-snort-cap!" More squeaks and snorts ensued until eventually silence was regained and they all began to look around. A domestic bookcase containing about 30 or so text books – a justification of the word 'library' painted on the doors – stood against one wall.

Above the empty fireplace a copy of Kiplings *If*, tastefully rendered in poker work, was displayed. In this version the last line 'We'll make a man of you' was replaced with 'We'll make a nurse of you'. H'mm, thought Margery, "Threat or Promise." Curiosity made her pick up a large book on the top of the bookcase. *Gray's Anatomy*. Her spirits fell. She'd seen this before – the medical students' bible. Surely, surely they wouldn't be required to study the subject to this depth? She flicked it open, it looked brand new and on the inside cover she read:

"Presented to the School of Nursing in gratitude for the skill, care and understanding shown to him during a recent illness.

Richard Carlisle 1944."

A well-meaning, but under-used and, she hoped, unnecessary gift!

Then someone noticed a pile of starched cotton triangles on the table. Caps!

Nicky tried draping one unsuccessfully over her head, posing for the rest to admire, but. . .

"Thank you. Nurse Knight," Sister Lumsden had entered. "Perhaps you will keep that particular cap for yourself, as you've crumpled it. Good morning everyone."

The class settled down and with practised ease Sister Lumsden demonstrated how to make a cap. Soon everyone had made and was wearing a cap and were manoeuvring to catch their reflection in the window. Black stockings *and* a cap. They were on their way!

The classroom was to be their workstation for the next few weeks and they looked around with interest. A low dais with lectern, a roll-over blackboard and Jimmy. Jimmy, Sister Lumsden informed them, seeing their interest, was the name of every mounted skeleton in every nurse training school in the country. The wired human skeleton hung from an armature on a stand, grinning back at them. This, several minds were recording, had once been a living, breathing person – not a plastic artefact to amuse on Halloween night. Hard to imagine and harder to accept, but there he hung for the education, stimulation and admiration of the student body!

Matron was expected. Some of the class had already met her at interview. To others she was an unknown quantity. A dragon? A disciplinarian? An 'in loco parentis' mother figure? Within minutes a voice could be heard on the corridor enquiring after Clarry's welfare and then a slim attractive woman of perhaps 40 plus years entered. Dressed in a severe navy blue dress, a little white lace at neck and wrists, and with a discreetly frilled cap, the effect was charming. The class dutifully rose and stood as one – they were learning.

Matron smiled round at everyone and welcomed them, "to our

training school, to this hospital, and to the profession." She wished them well, told them that she expected hard work and commitment to the patients in their care and to each other, and hoped that they would find their work interesting and rewarding. Her whole attitude indicated that they could do no other, would want to do no other and that they were privileged indeed to be given this opportunity. An opportunity they must not waste.

The class were mesmerised. Doreen, Michaela and several others were starry-eyed with anticipation of their chosen future. But then Matron changed tack. "I envy you all," she went on. "You are starting your careers at the birth of the National Health Service. There are going to be massive changes, in which you will have a part, to improve the medical and nursing care we can provide. The health of our nation is going to improve beyond all measure as the government takes on the burden of providing total care for every one of its population whether prince or pauper. Need will be the only criterion."

"Why already," she went on, "we are able to provide food, three nutritious meals a day, for our patients and they are no longer dependent on relatives bringing in their food on a daily basis." She paused. "And I have at the moment plans on my desk which provide for curtains that can be drawn around each bed, to not only allow patients a degree of privacy when performing their most intimate toilet functions, but to relieve *you* of the burden of carrying heavy screens up and down the wards. There are great times ahead and many challenges. I know you will be up to meeting them. I look forward to meeting you all again as a class, as you complete your preliminary training." With a nod at Sister Lumsden she was gone.

For a moment the class were stunned. Sister Lumsden, who had seen Matron in many moods, knew that she could be fierce, complaining, persistent in pursuit of slackness and strict in the face of what she called 'behaviour unfitting for a member of the nursing profession!' She had seen the effect she had had on new students before, and admired her for it, as indeed for her not inconsiderable capacities as a whole.

Lunch. She would be glad when this lot had got their bearings and leading them around like a bunch of schoolgirls would be unnecessary. She shepherded them to the dining room and departed for the sisters' table – leaving them to the tea, bread and jam provided.

No butter, no sugar, the 'rations' were back at Albert Terrace, but healthy young appetites made the best of what there was.

"Met the Scaly-Bott yet?" a second-year nurse obligingly wielding the tea pot enquired. The PTS nurse who had returned for a second cup looked blank. "Miss Bailey-Scott, Senior Tutor, a personage not to be missed. Not that you will be allowed to miss her – she'll see to that!" and the informant wandered off with her tea cup. What a splendidly rude name! This information had to be recounted and shared with the others, and gave the coming meeting with the Senior Tutor scheduled for the afternoon an added piquancy.

Returning to the classroom after lunch, the class found on the dais a large wooden box full of bones. A Jimmy-in-pieces. Sister Lumsden was placing a couple of exercise books on each desk. It looked as if the promised training was about to begin. Anatomy and physiology.

"We will start, as all students of this subject start, with the skeleton. The basis, the framework, the strength of the human body, without which we would all be formless blobs." Sister Lumsden was getting into her stride. "Leaving the skull till later we will start at the top of the thorax and consider every bone. I presume you all have writing implements?"

"No,"

"Has anyone a spare pen to lend to Nurse Knight? Thank you," as several were proffered. Really, she thought, what thickhead comes to a lecture without a pen.

Dictating information was not Sister Lumsden's idea of teaching, but needs must, so she launched into the name, function, position, relationship, articulation and muscle attachment of the clavicle, holding up a specimen of this small relatively unimportant bone, and pausing to write unfamiliar words on the blackboard as she went along. The class scribbled furiously.

Margery decided, as all this was already familiar to her, she would, for the sake of appearances, take a few notes. She had, after all, a fat file of information at home garnered during two years in the sixth-form.

"Nurse Harvey!" Margery jumped at this interruption in Sister

30

Lumsden's flow. "You are not taking this down?"

"I was writing notes, Sister."

"I'm afraid that that is not sufficient. Miss Bailey-Scott will want to see all your exercise books at the end of the week. She likes to know that you have been given the knowledge that the examining bodies require," and, she thought to herself, that I am feeding it to them, the old besom. "This hospital", Sister Lumsden continued, "has not the means to supply you each with a textbook, nor have student nurses the funds to buy their own, so in my sessions we are effectively compiling a substitute text book to which you can always refer.

"Some of you may be questioning the relevance of what we are recording today, that is relevance to work as some of you have experienced it on a ward. But think. If you are not familiar with the structure and functioning of the healthy body, how are you to understand the things that go wrong with it by way of disease or accident? And, if you don't understand that, how can you understand its treatment? Now, any questions so far?"

Sister Lumsden then switched her attention to the scapula. Margery, now recording every word that the tutor uttered, resorted to her own, tried and tested, form of shorthand. Margery wrote Scapula irr.b.sit.post.chest wall between ribs 2 & 7. Acromian, coracoid procs. Form glenoid cav. with hd. Humerus → shoulder jnt. A b & s jnt.

The definition of a lecture, heard or read somewhere, floated into Margery's mind:

"A lecture – the means by which the words on the tutor's notes are transferred to the pages of the student's notes, without passing through the minds of either." Very apt.

At last, after dealing with the humerus and sternum, Sister Lumsden called a halt for dinner. "Monday – so it's hotpot," she informed the class as they stood and stretched.

Hotpot. Kathleen O'Connor and Theresa McCall had never heard of it. The two had found each other within the group but had little in common beyond their Irish homeland. Kathleen, the city girl, had come to nurse training as a means of leaving home. Mum and Dad, both academics, had little understanding of their only daughter's lack of scholastic ambition and when she started to find a life outside the home in the pubs and clubs of Dublin's fair city, had attempted belatedly to notice her and establish

31

controls. Nursing in England, which, unlike the situation in Ireland, provided free training, accommodation and a wage (plus a new and exciting country thrown in) seemed an excellent solution to her difficulties in what she regarded as a stifling and stultified home life.

Hotpot turned out to be, in Theresa's estimation, a sort of Irish Stew and quite acceptable.

The dining room at dinner time assumed a formality not required at lunch, tea or supper times, with the nurses sitting in strict order of seniority on small tables ranging from those nearest the door – 1st years – round through second, third and fourth (Staff Nurse) years, then pupil midwives and, at the far end, the sisters dined, presided over by Matron. The PTS were on one long table at the side. Matron said grace to the standing assembly and the meal began, served by the maids who slapped down plates of hotpot with more speed than finesse. Everyone enjoyed the hotpot and then came pudding. Each and every day, December 25th being the only exception, the staff from consultants to resident maids, plus all the patients on every ward, had a choice of one of two puddings. Milk or sponge.

"Milk-ur-Spunge, Norse," the refrain was repeated up and down the room. Irish voices predominated.

"Milk-ur-Spunge, Norse," Milk or Sponge.

The maids, Sister Lumsden explained later, came over from Ireland in batches. Matron had an arrangement with the Mother Superior of an orphanage there for the supply of a quantity of eighteen year olds who required work and accommodation. Evidently the opportunity to travel to England and work at a hospital was much sought after and a big improvement on life in the alternative – laundries, also run by religious bodies. Who wouldn't choose, if given the opportunity, more freedom, more money, more life.

At the conclusion of the meal, Matron said the closing grace and walked out, followed in strict order of seniority by the rest of the staff, the PTS trailing humbly last – as befitted their lowly station.

Not welcome in the nurses' sitting room, where most retired for a quick smoke before returning to the wards, the PTS girls wandered back to the school, hung about the library and complained about Miss Bailey-Scott's 'No Smoking' rule.

One-forty-five and the much anticipated, as yet unseen, Miss Bailey-Scott was due to arrive. Then of course the formalities of this introductory day would be complete and they could get down to work.

When the lady did arrive a few minutes later, all eyes went to her cap. The most fascinating, the most ridiculous remnant of a nursing nun's wimple that one could imagine; irritating to wear and inviting of ridicule, but presumably Miss Bailey-Scott's choice, it resembled a crumpled paper bag trimmed with lace. At each side a broad white band came down to cover her ears and joined under her chin with a rigid bow. The smart grey dress, fine stockings and court shoes were mundane appendages to the glories of the cap.

Scaly-Bott indeed. Nothing could be less apt or more satisfactory! Her glance skimmed over the class, then seizing a piece of chalk, she went over to the blackboard and announced – "My name is Miss Bailey-Scott. I do *not* wish to be addressed as *Sister*," and she wrote MISS BAILEY-SCOTT on the board. She continued, "I am the senior tutor here and it is my responsibility to see that your training is effective, comprehensive and meets the requirements of the examining bodies. The next 4 weeks will be spent exclusively in school, in the following 4 weeks you will each spend half a day on the wards and in January, providing you are successful in the PTS exam you will start full-time work on the wards. Any questions?" – as if anyone would dare!

"Sister Lumsden, under my direction, is responsible for you in the next two months." Miss Bailey-Scott paused and brown eyes swept across the rows of desks as she continued – "A nurse's work is exhausting, physically, mentally and emotionally. You are young and healthy and you are expected to remain so – healthy that is. A sick nurse is no use to patient or colleague so it is your responsibility to maintain your strength with enough sleep, food, rest and fresh air. 'Off sick' are two words I do not recognise.

"Physically you will find the work very tiring. Mentally, you will be required to learn many things which will need study over and above attendance at lectures. Lastly, the emotional strain you will be under at times will be considerable. You will witness and be expected to help persons 'in extremis' either because of their own or their loved ones condition. In dealing with them you will never on any account show pity. Sympathy, compassion, understanding, *yes*, but *not* pity, for pity suggests no hope. At times you will want to cry. You will do so privately, out of sight; and when you have cried you will return to work where you are needed. It is said that nurses are 'hard'. Nurses are NOT hard – they have learnt to hide and control their emotions in order to do what is necessary. I expect nothing less of you."

The class were bemused, shocked at the difference between this woman's approach and that of Matron. Miss Bailey-Scott made her exit and the atmosphere relaxed.

"She doesn't wrap it up, does she?"

"I think I'll go home *now*."

"I have nothing to offer but blood, toil, tears and sweat."

"No late nights out dancing again, *ever*."

"First time anyone's mentioned a PTS exam."

"Bags me behind the sluice room door for a private crying place."

"You can't have that 'cos I'll be there having a fag."

In spite of the jocularity the Scaly-Bott's words had hit home. She had told it 'how it was' and the group were in no doubt that this was no place for softies.

As the Scaly-Bott retreated, up popped Sister Lumsden. At last the girls were going to meet a patient. This particular patient was a life-sized model sitting slightly upright in one of the two hospital beds – that is, two basic tubular metal bedsteads with regulation sponge rubber mattresses – that stood centrally in the practical demonstration room. There was also a cot containing a doll and numerous cupboards and shelves holding the impedimenta needed for nursing the sick.

Meet Mrs Green – who has had her bed made and simulated functions attended to by a succession of student nurses till her paint is peeling and her joints move creakily. The students watched while Sister Lumsden and one favoured student made the empty bed, setting up a rhythm working together that finished the job in no time. Pillows had had to be placed so that the open end of the pillow slip faced away from the ward door, bedding stripped, folded into three – draped over two chairs placed back to back the trailing ends on the door side to be folded under neatly. Top sheets must be placed having the hem underside down – the corners of each item of bedding must be folded to form a geometrical angle.

All this to preserve the tidy appearance of the ward. The eye of an incomer must not be offended by disorder lest the suspicion that the ward was not run with optimum efficiency be allowed to fester. To most of the students it came as a surprise to know that it was even possible to put on a sheet inside out!

Making a bed with the patient in situ was a little more complicated, though, as Sister Lumsden pointed out, Mrs Green only weighed about 20 pounds and didn't complain, so the task was comparatively easy.

Watch and learn, watch and learn. The students were keen to have a go, but more instruction was to follow. Those collective procedures known as 'toileting' and when it came to bed baths, trolley laying came into the picture. How could such simple procedures require such complicated methods and so much equipment – all of which it seemed must be cleaned and in some cases sterilised by the nurse concerned. Surely, surely thought some of those present, they weren't expected to launder the sheets? But no, Sister Lumsden explained. Stains must be soaked in cold water and solid matter, vomit and faeces, sluiced off before placing linen in a 'wet bin' and sending it to the laundry. Sluicing she emphasised was essential or the laundress would return the whole revolting, stinking bundle to the ward concerned – not a situation to please the sister-in-charge.

After a period of practice when Mrs Green was rollicked from side to side and sheets whizzed back and forth, the class re-gathered in the lecture room.

Michaela was having some difficulty managing to concentrate on all this reference directly or indirectly to body fluids. She wanted to know how to take a blood pressure, give an injection, and most of all she looked for an invitation into the drama of the operating theatre. She endured the current teaching with ill-concealed impatience and not a little disgust, but worse was to follow.

As the class settled down, Sister Lumsden began to teach, in contrast to the dictating of facts with which she had covered anatomy and physiology that morning.

"One of the nurse's main functions is to observe." She invited comment on this statement and slowly the class began to participate.

Appearance, behaviour, feelings, pain level, specific conditions, exudations, are to be noted and reported whilst carrying out those mundane tasks that had just been demonstrated – tasks that constituted the core element of nursing – that of making a patient comfortable.

"There is more to giving a patient a bed bath than applying soap and water." Words of wisdom. It was with the observation necessary when performing that humblest of tasks – emptying a bed pan – that Michaela met her Waterloo. Colour, consistency, amount, foreign bodies, worms, blood, mucus. All must be noted. Michaela closed her mind to the thought, the impossibility, of her rooting about in a pan full of liquid faeces and identifying parasitic worms. It was beyond belief that anyone should be expected to do this. Wasn't it?

The thought of eating/drinking what was on offer at 5pm, tea time, she found impossible and as some of the others were planning on catching the first house at the cinema, she went along with them trying to forget the previous few hours.

That night Michaela slept badly. She dreamt of Heinz Spaghetti – a dish that she quite enjoyed. But the sauce turned to blood and the spaghetti writhed obscenely on the toast and she woke with horror and revulsion flooding through her tired mind and body.

Meanwhile others, the day's labours over, walked back to Albert Terrace. Doreen's fire burned brightly, the radio played and Eileen set about finishing her letter to Kevin, the worrying thought of her inadequate attempts to put down on paper the dictated anatomy and physiology of the morning, pushed to the back of her mind.

Also penning a letter to her fiancé was Margaret Wood. A girl somewhat set apart from the rest, viewing their activities, comments and general behaviour with an interested tolerance, but adding little. Margaret, in coming to start nurse training, had begun the 'great four-year plan', as formulated by herself and her fiancé. She had no engagement ring, an expense deemed unnecessary by the couple whose intentions they felt concerned only themselves. Roger was now at theological college fulfilling a long-held conviction that he must give his life to the Church, and Margaret was right behind him. By the time she had qualified (and possibly done another year of midwifery training) Roger would have had some experience in his first curacy. Then they could look towards acceptance by a missionary society, and priest and nurse/midwife would embark on, what or where? That was in the hands of Him whom they sought to serve. Meanwhile they would wait, study and work.

At about 7.30pm it dawned on the half dozen or so individuals who had returned to Albert Terrace that if they were to eat again before breakfast tomorrow, they would have to trail once more back to the hospital. Dinner was six hours ago and the cup of tea and piece of slab cake offered at 5pm had been spurned by many, anxious to get away. Outside it was cold, dark, and yes, raining. This was definitely a drawback to life at Albert Terrace. Food, only available at certain times, was also only available a mile away. Money, a subject not usually spoken of in respectable society was scarce and as no one knew when pay day would be, so it had to be garnered carefully. So what to do? Then a brainwave. The chip shop! They could still afford 3d each and Margaret volunteered to sally forth, returning with a newspaper parcel, steaming and fragrant. They brewed tea, found half a sliced loaf in the kitchen, and those that still had some butter ration applied it thickly. A feast.

Margery, looking round at her chattering, laughing colleagues, eating with greasy fingers fragments of fried potato from their newspaper wrappings, felt supremely content with the life here. These girls, 24 hours ago, had been strangers, now they were friends with a common purpose. Thrown together by chance, they would work and play together, help each other through difficulties, support and counsel each other. Rejoice in triumphs, borrow each other's clothes, cover for each other in the face of authority. Every nurse knows what it means, when, years later, someone explaining a relationship says of another, "She was my PTS." The bond was forming.

Chapter Three

It was surprising really how quickly a routine established itself. On day two Margery was managing to make everyone's bed just a shade more quickly and could better keep up with Theresa's practiced tucking and folding. Eileen made sure that Nicky, with help from another, was removed from her bed and dumped on the floor. Doreen dusted and vacuumed and Jane made the fire.

Once established again in the classroom an announcement caused some consternation. Sister Lumsden told them they would finish work at dinner time, and the afternoon would be free. Smiles of delight flashed round, only to die as they were told they would then be expected to return to the school at 5pm and work till 8pm. An afternoon meant just that – three hours. Each Tuesday and Thursday, off duty would be 2–5pm. Monday, Wednesday and Friday they would work till 5pm, Saturday they would finish at 1.30pm, and Sunday would be a day off.

"Make the most of your weekends," Sister Lumsden instructed. "Once out of school you are unlikely to have many more – it will be a half and a day off mid-week, hopefully running concurrently, for some time to come. Staffing needs on the ward always come first – nurses' social lives a poor second."

What to do with three hours on a chilly November day! Nowhere in the hospital for the PTS to relax; lodgings a distance away and if they lit the fire there would be no coal (still rationed by the Ministry of Fuel and Power) for the evening. A walk in the park? Chilly. Go to the pictures, look at the shops. Needed money. Work in the library? Surely not.

After the usual physiology and anatomy there followed something called 'Health and Disease', another hour's lecture, dinner and then the class scattered to various pursuits. Theresa found Maeve Murphy in her room and gossiped happily. Eileen Downey and Margaret Woods wrote letters in the library and looked through the meagre collection of text books to see if they could find help with their A and P notes. Jane went home and the rest went into town shop window gazing. The gear up to Christmas was starting and this year there were some lights that were decorative and not completely essential. Things were improving. Walking back to Albert Terrace after supper (macaroni, cheese and a jam tart) it felt that a long long day had at last ended. Only 9pm, not really late, but somehow the 'split shift' had disorientated everyone and the fireside was well monopolised. What do young women do with time on their hands? They wash their hair, of course! Lots of hot water but no drying facilities except the one source of heat in the house, the common room fire. For years afterwards the smell of newly washed hair overladen by that of setting lotion, would bring back, for Margery, the common room at Albert Terrace – and the perpetual hairdressing that went on there.

The week ground on, with no suggestion that pay-packets were forthcoming. The message gleaned from Theresa's friends, the Murphy sisters (who were second-year students and therefore very knowledgeable) was that it would be month-end before anything could be expected. Very worrying, especially as regards to having the wherewithal to get home at the weekend. Everyone except the Irish girls lived within a twenty mile radius of Merton and would expect to have days off at home. Pennies were counted and re-counted. Essential needs like sanitary towels, toothpaste, deodorants and so on were estimated. The smokers were in the greatest difficulties. Money for food (in addition to that provided in the dining room), make-up, and for pleasure pursuits in general just would not be available for another three weeks.

Saturday morning domestic chores were performed in cheerful anticipation of finishing at dinner time for a whole half and then day off. The group gathered as usual in the school expecting the daily dose of anatomy and physiology, but instead of the cheerful

39

Sister Lumsden, Clarry appeared carrying a crate of cleaning materials. Saturday mornings it seemed the PTS were required to clean the training school, and Clarry was in charge. She waddled about importantly distributing cleaning materials, and issuing instructions. The demonstration room, lecture room, library, corridor and toilet were left to the tender mercies of eleven energetic young women, who had had a week of hard work and new experiences and were ready for some light relief.

They buffed the floor and slid on it. They pushed a feather duster up between Jimmy's legs and dusted his inside – the biggest thrill he'd had in a 100 years. Audrey Manning, a duster at the ready in her left hand, wrote on the blackboard in her best copper-plate script "Scaly-Bott, Scaly-Bott, call me Sister you MUST NOT". They cleaned the windows and either made faces or blew kisses to passers-by. Clarry knew when she was beaten and returned to the kitchen, she'd seen this before. Hysteria. As dinner time approached the rooms were returned to order and had, indeed, been cleaned by the more sober members of the class.

Michaela Green viewed these riotous proceedings with mixed feelings. She still rebelled against the use of herself, and her colleagues as domestic drudges, even though as it was pointed out, it was their own premises they were cleaning for their own benefit. She'd got over the bedpan horrors but her high ideals were becoming more and more tattered. The bedpan horrors had resurfaced when they'd spent a whole session on the prevention of bed sores. Some of the pictures they had been shown of raw, cavernous wounds were nightmarish. If this wasn't enough there had followed instruction on the giving of enemas. Was a nurse's working life totally obsessed with bowels? It would seem so. Michaela was having doubts of her ability to deal with such things. She was, after all, she reasoned, a creature of some sensitivity and refinement. Perhaps it was this very refinement that was preventing her accepting her vocation. That weekend, Michaela re-read Ngaio Marsh's book *Green for Danger* in an attempt to revive the hospital mystique that had so captivated her. She failed dismally, reality had bitten hard. She wrote her letter of resignation to Matron and disappeared from the lives of her erstwhile colleagues forever. She had lasted just one week.

The girls came bouncing back on Sunday night, Michaela's absence neither surprised nor troubled them. Several had managed to borrow from parents or boyfriends, cash to help them over the next three weeks. Several also brought back some of their mum's baking, a sacrifice indeed in households still rationed for sugar and fats. Nicky stumbled in at 10.28pm not happy because Arthur had told her it would be Wednesday before he came again – selfish pig. Kathleen O'Connor had been to the Irish Club in town on Saturday night and met a *fantastic* man who had a car. The company were lost in envy. Audrey Manning had dumped her chap – good riddance. On and on it went. Do young women living together ever run out of conversation?

Different chores on Monday morning as the rota – just rotated! What would week two bring? Well, firstly on arriving at school a summons for Nicola Knight and Margery Harvey to Miss Bailey-Scott's presence. The previous Thursday everyone's anatomy and physiology note books had been collected for Scaly-Bott's inspection, and all but Margery's and Nicky's were returned.

Nicola emerged from the Senior Tutor's room looking defiant. Margery was genuinely puzzled as to why she had been called. She met a steely pair of eyes, her note book on the blotter. "What is this?" peremptory tones. It was perfectly obvious what 'this' was, and Margery hesitated. "I can't read it," Miss Bailey-Scott continued to glare. Relief dawned, as Margery realised that it was her self-devised shorthand that the tutor objected to.

"No, but I can – read it, that is, and surely that is what is important?" Margery faltered.

"Are you being impertinent, Nurse?" Miss Bailey-Scott was trying to recall this girl's CV. Of course, she remembered now that she had a higher school certificate. "You may consider your note-taking superior to that of others, but I will not have you resting on doubtful laurels acquired elsewhere. You will write Sister Lumsden's lectures out in full, like everyone else, so that I can ensure that we are fulfilling our obligations to train you." She gave a nod of dismissal.

Margery sighed. Copying out notes when she already had a file full and text books at home was annoying in the extreme. What a bore.

The weeks progressed, but an upheaval as week three was drawing to a close occupied everyone's attention to the exclusion of everything else.

Arthur had duly roared up on his newly tuned bike on

Wednesday evening and carried off his lady love, quite to what, was left to the imagination of anyone sufficiently interested to consider. On Thursday morning Eileen Downey had woken to find Nicky's bed empty, and still neatly made. Eileen had gone to bed to read, fallen asleep, doused the light and knew no more until Anne's 6.30am call. Could Nicky possibly have got up and started on the 'domestics' having first made her bed? This seemed unlikely in the extreme, so Eileen got up, checked this, and then enquired of the others sleepily starting on the morning's chores. She checked the signing-in book in the hall; Nicky's name in her illiterate scrawl was at the top of the list for last night. This, of course, meant nothing. It had soon dawned on the company that to obviate forgetting to 'sign in' on returning to the house and thus earning a reprimand, the wisest thing was to sign oneself 'in' before one went 'out', and that was probably what Nicky had done. Eileen thought that possibly Nicky had gone home, but with no way of checking, she had no option but to report her room mate as missing and let someone else sort it out. The girl was a liability.

Sister Lumsden, on receiving Eileen's information, felt the weight of her responsibility. She questioned the nurses, all as mystified as each other, and decided to wait till after breakfast before taking this further. The girl was a waste of time, as far as she was concerned, and though she didn't wish her injured, or lying in a ditch somewhere, a victim of Arthur's driving skills, she would like to see her gone from this most unsuitable placement in the nurse training school.

At 7.15am Nicky appeared at the door, not yet unlocked for the day, dirty, cold crumpled and defiant. Asking for an explanation, Sister Lumsden had difficulty in believing Nicky's in part, truthful, story. She and Arthur had spent the night under the bandstand in the adjacent park. The bit about 'forgetting the time' and knowing it would be useless to return after 10.30pm, were just embellishments. Arthur, it seemed, had had his wicked way, on the cold concrete floor of the Victorian bandstand, fully encouraged by Nicky. A night of passion in extremely uncomfortable conditions, Nicky seemed smugly self-satisfied with her behaviour. Arthur's 'neglect' as she saw it, forgotten. He was hers! Sister Lumsden sent her for a wash, a change and some breakfast. She would have to think about this.

42

Mid morning the summons came. Nurse Knight to Matron's office, please; and Nurse Knight's dismissal followed rapidly. Goodbye to school, hospital and career.

It wasn't the first time that Matron had found it necessary to sack a student, but usually she felt it keenly as a failure on her and her staff's parts in either poor selection or poor teaching. But in this case, Nurse Knight's unsuitability was evident in the first few days of her contract. She had been the last in a batch of ten girls that the Matron of a small hospital in a neighbouring town had agreed to send for training in Merton; training that her own hospital could not provide. Nursing auxiliaries with the aspirations and, she judged, the capabilities to go further. Well, in this case she had judged wrongly.

"Lack of commitment, laziness, poor classroom work and now the flagrant flouting of rules." Matron was cool, positive, and for appearances sake, regretful. She didn't beat about the bush.

"You will return to Albert Terrace and pack up your belongings. I calculate that you are entitled to two days' holiday pay – I am being generous in that. It will be included in your end of month salary which the finance department will have ready for you."

Nicky's jaw dropped. Sacked! Then her inbred antagonism to authority and to class differences asserted itself and she screamed: "You can keep your bloody job and your so called training. Is humping coal up cellar steps 'training' or exploitation? Is standing and practically curtseying to the likes of you? Training – to become like you? – a dried up old spinster – I don't think so. You need to get a life, chum."

Sister Lumsden, sitting with Matron, curled up in embarrassment, but Matron didn't seem at all disturbed. "If', she replied pleasantly, "getting a life means behaving like a bitch on heat in an empty park bandstand, then I think I will stay with my present one!"

Nicky stamped out.

Matron turned to Sister Lumsden and asked mildly, "What's all this about humping coal?" Sister Lumsden explained what the morning chores entailed. "Hm," said Matron, "they shouldn't have to do that. Requisition another coal scuttle, two trips with half a load will be easier." Matron never ceased to surprise.

Week four, and poverty was endemic. No one took the bus,

43

now, in the mornings. Shampoo and toilet soap was shared by those who still had some. Margaret Woods, the only one who had had the foresight to bring mending materials from home, handed out lengths of black cotton and stockings were darned. Anne Manning, to whom any kind of sewing was an anathema, tried putting black shoe polish on her heels to disguise the moon of flesh that revealed a hole. This, the rest decided, was going too far and was too messy.

It was at the start of week four that the grand scheme to raise cash was devised. Audrey Renton, a smoker, had pawned her watch, which she was hoping to retrieve before she worked on the wards and needed to count pulses. Pawning was a new idea to most of the nurses, who had known such shops existed but had never sought one out, and they started to look around their possessions for anything which might be a possibility. Then a brilliant thought came to Jane Kirkham. The *Gray's Anatomy* book in the library that no one ever used might be worth a bob or two. They could sign it out as 'borrowed', raise money on it at the pawn shop and retrieve it when pay day came. Wow! Who would sign it out? It was decided that it had better be Margery Harvey, the most likely amongst a bunch of unlikely scholars to borrow such a tome. Margery wasn't happy about it, and worried until she had the book back, but went along with the plan for the sake of her penniless friends. The scheme worked, £10!

The book made the trip again in December, after which 'uncle' started asking questions. So the book took up its permanent place in the library again.

The grateful patient who had donated the book, of course, never knew how useful his gift had been. But best of all – the scheme was done under the noses of those powers-that-be who would no doubt have considered it 'a deed unbecoming to a member of the profession' and reacted accordingly.

The 'Health and Disease' lectures were becoming sessions of discovery. They had started off with 'What is health?' – an abstract concept never contemplated by most of the class. Discussion dismissed 'Health is not being ill' and 'Health is having a good doctor', and eventually they arrived at 'Health is a state of mental, physical and emotional wellbeing and NOT just an absence of disease'. They were beginning to think, and not just imitate or absorb without thought or question. Having satisfactorily dealt

44

with 'Health' they could then move on to 'Disease'. Why? How? What? They could see that although the S.D.T.P. (symptoms, diagnosis, treatment, prognosis) of specifics would come later, there was a mountain of knowledge to be explored in generalisations. Old wives' tales were demolished after the crumbs of truth contained therein were extracted and examined. Binding a piece of mouldy cheese onto a suppurating wound was laughable – but wasn't penicillin produced from mould, so – not so daft, though, as was pointed out – we have moved on somewhat in the fight against infection and no longer use 'cheese therapy'!

Half way. Four weeks. Now all thoughts were focusing on the following Saturday when the first tentative steps onto real wards with real patients were anticipated. The list was read out on Friday as the afternoon session drew to a close. Margery was relieved to find herself allocated to Lister Ward, a women's surgical. Of course she knew she must and was quite willing to nurse men, but for this first foray into this largely unknown world she felt she would be happier with the women. Doreen Melling and Kathleen O'Connor were to go to Jenner Ward, a medical ward, the largest in the hospital, sixty-two beds, split into two wards known as 'male end' and 'female end'. Jenner Ward was notorious. Not only did it have the fiercest and longest serving sister, but also the ill-est patients and therefore the heaviest work and the highest death rate in the hospital. The rest of the class were spread similarly across other medical and surgical wards and of course the children's ward. Private patients and specialist wards were staffed by second year trainees and theatre and casualty by those in their third year, so none featured as PTS experience.

Pay day came at last, and there was, at least for a few days, money jingling in pockets. Christmas was looming and with it the need to buy presents for mums, dads and little brothers and sisters at the minimum. A worry to be shelved for later. Where would they all be at Christmas? Back home having failed the end of PTS exam perhaps. "Not a chance," said that mine of information the Murphy twins. "Everyone always passes. You're needed to fill the gap left by those students that leave before their finals – for easier, better paid jobs, to live at home, and to get married. Or they just vanish without trace. Everyone moves up and you join the end. You'd have been sent packing by now. They wouldn't have wasted their time training you, if they were going to fail you at the end. There were ten of us started in our PTS but only five finished. Your lot have done OK. Only two gone – yet."

Work in the school was one thing, but the coming work on the wards another. Surely their willingness and competence would also be assessed and possibly found wanting.

"A little knowledge is a dangerous thing!" Alexander Pope's wise words still applied. There were those who thought the previous four weeks had fitted them for anything, and would be quite willing to take on running the ward. Others who, like Margery, were overwhelmed by their own *lack* of knowledge felt totally unprepared to function adequately. What *would* it be like?

Lister Ward was a moderately sized Nightingale Ward. That is, 10 beds faced 10 beds; patients gazed across at other patients, the windows between beds, high and inaccessible. At the end, one either side, two small single rooms, and between them a short passage leading through to clinic room, sluice room, bathroom and toilet. At the opposite end of the ward, the kitchen, and a tiny pocket of a room barely large enough to hold a desk and three upright chairs – Sister's office.

It was here that Margery joined three others to get her first taste of ward work. In the adjacent kitchen a middle aged woman was starting to wash a trolley full of used crockery, steam rising from a large wooden sink. Night staff were nowhere to be seen. The staff nurse, by reason of her seniority sat at the office desk, while the rest of the day staff craned over her shoulders to read the night report compiled by the sole student nurse who had had responsibility for the care of the 22 patients for the last ten hours. What Margery could see of the report meant less than nothing to her. What on earth were all the acronyms, abbreviations, and initials all about? Morph. ¼ 23 hrs. C.S., N.P.U. This made her shorthand, as deplored by Miss Bailey-Scott quite intelligible. Margery gathered from others' comments, rather than from the report, that an Anne Smith aged 15 had been admitted in the small hours with a possible appendicitis. She was reported as 'comfortable' and would be seen this morning by someone more experienced than the house man who had admitted her. She would possibly have the offending appendage removed today. Little else in the night report registered.

"Another pair of hands," the staff nurse acknowledged her

"Goodo," and Margery was put under the supervision of a first year student who could boast a whole four months' experience. So far, in her short career, Nurse Horsfield, known colloquially and rather offensively as 'Horsey', had always been the most junior of juniors, so she took to guiding and mentoring Margery with enthusiasm. At last! Someone who knew even less than herself. "Beds," she announced and she and Margery started on one side of the ward, whilst their two colleagues tackled the other one. Beds were stripped twice a day, first thing in the morning, again in later afternoon with numerous straightenings and tidyings between. The first two beds they were to make were easy. The first held a good looking woman who, a week ago, had had her gall bladder removed. "Cholecystectomy," announced Nurse Horsfield. "Female, fit, fat, fair, flatulent and forty."

" 'Ere not so much of the fat, and I'm not forty till next year," grumbled the patient.

Nurse Horsfield grinned. "Don't mind me. You know we all love you, fit or fat. "This is a new Nurse," she went on – "so be nice to her." Then to Margery, "Gall bladders often match the six 'Fs', just as this lady does.

Bed number two was empty, its occupant, a bulky dressing on her neck, was sitting alongside in a chair. "Thyroidectomy," Nurse Horsfield announced – she was enjoying this opportunity to air her knowledge – but when they came to the third bed more difficulties presented. The patient was huge, her bulk flowed over the bed, her chest and upper left arm swathed in bandages. Propped up on pillows and with a drip feed attached to one ankle, she looked as if she wouldn't, couldn't, hadn't moved since she had been deposited there unconscious, straight from theatre. How inadequate as a teaching aid was the light-weight, small sized Mrs Green of the training school when faced with this sort of dilemma. They lifted, they rolled, they heaved. The patient moaned, protested her inability to help herself and was coaxed, threatened with dire complications if she didn't move herself a little and rolled again. Eventually her bottom sheet was changed, her pressure areas treated (wow! what pressure! 15 stones!). She was left clean and comfortable, if exhausted. "And patients like that," said 'Horsey' as they moved on, "are the reason why all nurses who stay in bedside nursing until they retire at 55 do so with injured backs."

In the last bed, the newly arrived Anne Smith lay curled up, miserable and frightened. As they approached, she turned over and faced them, alarm in her eyes. "I'm all right now, I've not been sick and the pain's better, so I can go home, can't I?"

"That's not for us to say," Nurse Horsfield explained. "Cheer up, Dr Carr will see you soon and he'll decide. He's very nice, you'll like him."

"I don't want no operation and I'm hungry, but they wouldn't give me no breakfast."

Nurse Horsfield explained why to Margery. She turned to the frightened girl, "Not long to wait now." Margery would have liked to stay and reassure her, but time didn't allow such luxury.

"And now," announced 'Horsey', "the sluice. Your domain. Clean it. Empty the steriliser. Clean it, and put the contents back. I'll do bathroom and clinic room and see to the flowers. OK?" Flowers, for some ill explained reason had to be taken out each evening, housed in the bathroom and returned, their water changed in the morning. Something to do with their exuding carbon dioxide and gobbling up oxygen. Vague reasons, rigid routine, and a blooming (ha! ha!) nuisance.

Margery regarded the sluice quizzically. A sort of sink-cum-lavatory. It had taps, a lever and a chain. Tentatively Margery bent and tried pushing the level and immediately a jet of cold water shot into the air, soaking her face, hair and cap. She let out a squawk that brought the staff nurse, busy doing something important in the clinic room, running to see what was amiss.

"You only touch the lever when you are cleaning a bed pan and it's upturned over the jet," she snapped and disappeared again. *Now* where was her friend and advisor? Walking around putting flowers on lockers as her newly acquired seniority allowed. Margery struggled on. "Be quick, get a move on, hurry up, we have to get the lockers done before Sister does her morning round. Move faster, walk quicker," exhortations from one whose routine jobs on the ward each morning were always too numerous to fit into the time available for their completion. With Margery's advent these were shared, but a novice could be something of a hindrance too. Soon Margery was initiated into what 'doing the lockers' entailed. Collect in water jugs and glasses, remove rubbish and extraneous crockery and wipe the tops, but also 'find my slippers', 'shake my pillows', 'pick up my magazine, admire my photos, jobs which were demanded of the nurses because they were there and which intruded into the task in hand. Soon the loaded trolley was pushed into the kitchen for the ward maid to wash and refill the jugs while the two nurses cleaned the hand basins, changed towels and renewed the bowl of Dettol standing waiting to receive used face masks.

"You did fill the intake and output charts didn't you?"

Margery looked back blankly at Nurse Horsfield.

"Oh lordy, you haven't!"

Patiently as to a half-witted child, the signs stating 'Note fluid balance' were pointed out on four beds that Margery had dealt with.

"You estimate how much of the 40 fluid ounce jug the patient had drunk and you WRITE IT DOWN – and you enter every cup of fluid you give subsequently. That's the intake, output you also measure from every bed pan and record it."

Smarting from the withering tone and her own failure to carry out a job she hadn't known existed – the first of many – Margery asked, "What shall I do?"

"Go round and ask the patients how much they drank overnight." Looking at Margery's crestfallen face, Nurse Horsfield relented, "Don't worry, its not the first time that's happened."

At 9.30am Margery was sent by the staff nurse for her mid-morning break, leaving Horsey to make Ovaltine for everyone and distribute that and the refilled water jugs. It was on her return that Margery was met by an angry Nurse Horsfield who had just received a thorough telling off from the sister, who, seeking to prepare for her morning round, inspecting and renewing dressings, removing stitches and clips and such, had found the steriliser and its contents cold and not sterile.

"For goodness sake. Have you no common sense?" Nurse Horsfield was cross. "I'm going for my break now and I haven't done the bed pan round, so get on with that – you do *know* how to give a bed pan, I presume?" The sarcasm was painful. Margery sped off. Up and down, up and down, soon eight women were perched on the eight bed pans that the ward possessed – then:

"NURSE HARVEY!" It was Sister, walking through to the clinic room. "CLOSE THE WARD BEFORE YOU GIVE OUT BED PANS."

49

c

Margery froze. She'd no idea what was meant by this.

"Put a screen across the door: Would you like all and sundry to walk in and watch you on the toilet?"

"No Sister, sorry Sister." Margery lugged a screen across the door. Empty, squirt, warm, dry and take the next one out. It was when the last patient had been relieved of her noxious receptacle and all bed pans were returned to the racks that Margery, with a frisson of horror, remembered the 'outputs' – what to do? Seeing Nurse Horsfield's return was like greeting a long lost, if prickly, friend. She was blasé about Margery's lapse.

"Guess it," she said wearily. This guiding and mentoring lark had to include instructions on subterfuge, short cuts and covering for each other in the face of authority, didn't it?

"Now," continued the long suffering, Nurse Horsefield, "every junior nurse's responsibility is the back book. We treat pressure areas twice a day, some more often, and record any sign of incipient soreness in the book. Right? Off you go!"

Setting off with the trolley and the back book, Margery's legs, feet and shoulders were protesting. Three hours continuous motion, two and a half still to go. 'Doing backs' – a euphemism for rubbing bottoms, applying methylated spirit and talcum powder – an attention appreciated by most patients who were, on the whole, tolerant and 'patient' with the new nurse.

A diversion in the midst of all this rubbing was the arrival of Dr Carr to see Anne Smith. Gosh! But he was a looker, straight from the silver screen! Margery was sneaking admiring glances at this Adonis in a white coat, when, "Screens, Nurse!" the order was snapped out by the accompanying sister. Margery ran to comply.

Dr Carr was palpitating Anne's abdomen and questioning her about her diet. No, she never ate vegetables, didn't like fruit, never had porridge or cereal. He asked for a glove, and to Anne's embarrassment and horror examined her rectally. By now she was sobbing, not in pain, but at the ignominy of her position in this nasty ward with nasty people who did unspeakable disgusting things. But Dr Carr was a kind young man. He patted her hand and told her to cheer up – she could go home. Walking back to the office he gave his diagnosis and instruction. "Chronic constipation – give her an enema and talk to her mum about her diet. A diet sheet wouldn't come amiss."

So that was the next job for a junior nurse. Whether Margery or Anne was the more nervous it was hard to tell – but the enema was managed without flooding the bed with soapy water and in spite of the patient's unwillingness to co-operate. Nurse Horsfield supervised!

Dinner time. Beds were tidied, trays set, patients who could do so helped to sit up, and into the ward was pushed the dinner trolley and plugged in to keep things warm. Sister served, spooning out meat and vegetables which the nursing staff carried round. Those on light diet got either minced chicken or stewed tripe, it was hard to tell the difference – both a sort of beige mess – and for that matter not unlike the milk pudding that followed. Eye appeal to tempt appetite was there not.

Another bed pan round – this time followed by wash bowls. Twenty-two patients, eighty-eight, or thereabout, trips to fetch and to empty. Today was visiting day so patients worried about their appearance before facing loved ones. Margery could no longer feel her legs and feet. Her shoulders ached, her back ached, even her face ached from the effort of keeping it cheerful. Nurse Horsfield went to dinner at 12.45pm – she still had another three and a half hours to work in the afternoon; Margery would be free at 1.30pm.

At the staff nurse's direction she stripped Anne Smith's now empty bed, washed the bed frame and the rubber mattress cover with weak carbolic and made up the bed afresh. She found patients' clean nighties and bed jackets, helped comb the hair of a woman whose hands were twisted with rheumatism, and brought another bed pan, plus a screen, for a lady who apologetically explained that she couldn't 'go' after dinner, but felt she could do so now, before her visitors arrived.

At last Nurse Horsfield and another new face arrived back from dinner, the new nurse would be working through from now until 10pm. Margery was free to go – that is when she had asked politely and submissively for permission to do so. No one wished her a nice weekend, thanked her for her effort, hoped that her first ward experience had been a good one. She had been snapped at and harassed, urged to move faster, accused of omissions and mistakes. The patients had sometimes said 'thank you', but on the whole were apprehensive, and aware of her inexperience and therefore distrustful. And she had never, ever, felt so utterly exhausted in her life. How ever would she manage, as she would have to do when training school days were over and she had to work on to 5pm?

Walking down the corridor to the dining room, Margery spied in front of her a small blue-clad figure who seemed to be having difficulty in walking in a straight line, tottering from side to side of the wide corridor. Doreen Melling. Margery pushed her tired legs to go a bit faster and caught her up. "Hello," – speech died as she took in Doreen's appearance and then: "Are you alright, Doreen?"

The pale face, now de-nuded of make up, glistened with a film of perspiration. Hair falling in rat-tails below a crumpled cap clung in places to her cheeks, her apron damp and stained. Doreen's face, like her small neat body, sagged.

"Yes, I'm OK. Just tired," and she smiled weakly.

"Hm, me too." Strangely Margery's weariness seemed less in the face of Doreen's extreme exhaustion and she attempted to rally her. "You're probably hungry, you'll feel better after some of that beautiful milk-ur-spunge." A weak attempt at a joke; ignored.

"No, I'm going home, my father's picking me up."

"Even better – your mum's cooking."

Margery left her to go down to the dining room. Food, she was ravenous, and then home. She would think about the morning's experience when she'd eaten and had a rest. The thought of her bed was enticing but she still had the long weary walk back to Alfred Terrace before her. Perhaps when she'd had her dinner, the bus. . .

Chapter Four

"It gets better, you know – improves, that is, as your body adjusts." Audrey Renton was giving the girls, all returned on Sunday evening to Albert Terrace, the benefit of her previous experience at 'Mary's'. "It's the same every time you return from holiday, two or three days of utter exhaustion before you begin to feel that your body is your own again, and there is some existence beyond bed and work."

"I should jolly well hope so," grumbled Kathleen.

Jane, Margery and Doreen, all nodded their agreement. They were back to normal functioning and looking, in retrospect, at their various mornings on the wards. Next Saturday they would know what to expect – or would they? Whatever else the work was, they all agreed, it wasn't boring. When the raw material of your job is people, anything could, and did, occur. Then the first of many, many, conversations started:

"On the ward we had – "

"What do you think came in on Saturday – "

"So and so happened on the ward. . ."

"We did this, we did that."

The learning from each other, the grumbling, the laughing at situations that could easily be seen as disasters – the black comedy – and so on. At least three others had been baptised, like Margery, by the sluice and had caps collapsed by cold water jets. Jane had been caught sneaking a drink of left-over Ovaltine behind the kitchen door and had been soundly reprimanded. "Eating on the wards is verboten; you know."

"What, not even a toffee?"

"Well possibly a toffee if you chew quietly!"

Anne had had the presence of mind to accept with thanks an almost full pack of cigarettes from a chap whose backside she had rubbed to his satisfaction. She didn't smoke, but why look a gift horse in the mouth when others did? – and she tossed the packet across. There followed a discussion on whether it was ethical to accept presents from patients.

"Of course," said Audrey.

"No," said Margaret Woods. "It's like tipping, not on, and undignified."

"Couldn't manage without it." This was Theresa.

"Then they should pay us more," Audrey again. "And what about the need to steal?"

Steal! Audrey's question was meant to shock.

"M'm," she went on. "Sanitary Towels: I never bought any the whole time I was at 'Mary's'!"

This continual recital of the joys of working at 'Mary's' was getting as boring as Arthur's bike had been.

"Well if you choose to work in women's gynae and get paid in sanitary towels that's your affair – I prefer money myself." Anne never failed to produce a quip, or a put-down. It seemed this business of nursing provided many opportunities for hilarity as well as aching limbs.

Margery had spent some time over the weekend thinking through her morning on Lister Ward. It took a while to sort out in her mind the hectic rush through the work, and gasping, metaphorically speaking, to keep pace. The constant anxiety she had found trying. Anxiety lest she forgot or omitted to do something that, though in the grand scheme of things, might seem unimportant, nevertheless held repercussions for patients' comfort and their ultimate recovery. Did she look forward to next Saturday? Well yes, sort of. She wanted to know more; how well or badly would these patients progress and why? Her interest had been aroused and though she had smarted under criticism (in part undeserved) and ended the morning practically dead with fatigue, her overwhelming feeling was one of satisfaction.

What worried her the most was her monumental ignorance of

54

much of what she saw around her. She wouldn't forget to chart intake and output again after this week's default, but she didn't know why it had to be done. What was wrong with those individuals? Why had the woman with the bandaged chest got a drip in her foot, what was being dripped in and why, what purpose did it serve? Margery knew she was addressed as 'Nurse', and was dressed like one (sort of) but she also accepted that in her own estimation she knew nothing – or very nearly nothing. Would what she learnt in theory keep pace with demands made on her on the wards? She doubted it. Staffing levels didn't allow for sufficient instruction, or supervision, 'on the job' and the possibility of what she may be expected to do she found frightening. Was everyone more capable of coping than she was herself, or better at hiding their ignorance? Or even, for that matter, not aware of their own infallibility? Only time would tell.

In their fifth week, the group received some wonderful news. Not only were they to be allocated a week's holiday over Christmas, but they were to be paid for December on the 22nd of the month instead of on the last day. Eileen Downey was ecstatic. Her fiancé (he whom she always referred to as 'my young man') had written to say that he was expecting some home leave over the Christmas holiday, and now they would be spending it together. Margaret Woods too could look forward to time with her husband-to-be at this blessed season. Of the rest only Kathleen O'Connor did not rejoice. She had no wish to go home and spend Christmas with her parents. Her relationship with the young man (he of the car ownership) who she had met shortly after arriving in Merton, had blossomed. They had exciting plans for Christmas parties and dances, which she was loath to forego. Would it be convenient, she asked Sister Lumsden, to continue to stay at Albert Terrace? This, she was told, was not possible, as it was intended to start installing central heating there before the next PTS arrived. Perhaps, Kathleen was told, she would like to apply to Matron for accommodation at the hospital?

It took a while for Kathleen to concoct her story, but at last she had it ready – she couldn't go home as her parents were on a lecture tour in the USA and had let their house on a short term contract to a colleague of theirs. She had no other family and didn't want to impose on friends. Could Matron find her a room in the nurses' home a week earlier than the rest of her school?

Matron swallowed the story whole and told Kathleen she would find her a room, and invited her to join in any special functions organised by the hospital over the Christmas period. She 'felt sorry for the girl' Matron confided to Sister Lumsden who answered "Yes," – dryly and nothing more. It was no longer the tutor's responsibility – soon she would have another intake of young hopefuls to worry about.

If Kathleen was anxious *not* to go home, her compatriot was just the opposite. Theresa's difficulty was that if she was to secure a passage on the often over-subscribed boat to Ireland she needed to buy her ticket *now* and she didn't have the wherewithal. Every red-blooded Irishman (and woman) adrift within a reasonable distance of the homeland, attempted the journey back there at Christmas. Theresa ached for it. She had never wanted anything so badly in her life as her familiar home and family. She telegraphed her difficulty to her dad and waited anxiously. Within a few days the reply came: "Boat tickets in the post." She was going home.

The days now were accelerating towards further Saturday mornings on the wards and ultimately the end-of-school exam. The girls were becoming almost old hands in their identity as student nurses. Margery found herself running informal tutorials, a posh name she secretly allowed herself to use, tutorials on physiology and anatomy. To so many, these subjects were the bête noires of their endeavours, subjects with which Margery was familiar. She struggled with more practically based knowledge and was still indeed struggling with the Saturday mornings' ward work.

If Margery was having a difficult time on the ward, one even more so was Doreen Melling allocated to Jenner Ward. She had started off well with bed making and all the routines common to all wards. Familiarity with the sluice room was the lot of every junior nurse and Doreen expected that. She fetched and carried. Bedpans, bottles, bowls, screens, drinks and meals, the never-ending round with which she coped cheerfully. Then, on her second Saturday morning, she was told to take Monica to the bathroom for her thrice weekly wallow in the warm soapy water of the large slipper bath, a treat that gave the girl much pleasure in a life not replete with such indulgences. Monica was 16 years old, but was small for her age. Juvenile arthritis had twisted and shrunk her limbs, the joints in contrast were large and knobbly. She suffered almost constant pain which showed on her pinched face, and she came into hospital from time to time, in part to give her mother some respite, but mainly for rest, physiotherapy and adjustment of her pain relief medication.

"Prepare the bath, get her things together, bring her in a wheelchair and give me a shout when she's ready and I'll help you get her in." The nurse immediately senior to Doreen was organising the extra hands Doreen's presence provided, then left her to get on with the job, retiring herself for a quiet smoke in the toilet.

Doreen had learned about filling baths. The cold in first then add hot water till it reached – she couldn't quite remember the exact temperature needed – but there was the bath thermometer in its wooden case, so she dipped it in and it seemed OK.

Get a wheelchair, collect toiletries and towels and hang them on the chair back, push it close to the bed. Then what? But Monica knew the ropes and took charge.

"Take the half plaster off me legs and swing me legs over the side. Now sit me up and put me slippers on. Now put your arms round under mine and heave me onto the chair."

Doreen was 5' 2" and slender, but needs must, so she did just that and it was then that the disaster happened. As soon as Monica's bottom touched the chair it shot backwards into the middle of the ward. Doreen, straining to hold the girl's weight, managed to hang onto her and control her descent onto the floor – then lost her own balance and sprawled full length on top of the girl. Monica howled. The two patients in beds opposite, who had been watching the proceedings with bored indifference, started to bellow for a nurse. Others took up the shout and pandemonium reigned.

Nurses came, of course, three of them. They picked up and soothed Monica, putting her, swathed in blankets, into the retrieved chair. Doreen, ignored by everyone, picked herself up and stood shaking with shock and horror at the side. Eventually the staff nurse turned to her. "Brakes, Nurse. Wheelchairs have brakes, you put them on before you attempt to lift a patient." The tone was cold, the exasperation barely controlled. Doreen was left convinced of her own ineptitude, lack of common sense, and of course, of the pain and fright she had caused Monica to suffer.

To the bathroom now, with another nurse to help and direct. Monica's nightdress was removed and, in the chair, her legs supported horizontally as she was pushed up to the bath's foot. The idea was that, with a nurse either side, Monica would be slid down the slope and into the water. It reached her ankles only before she let out a yell. The water was cold. Never perhaps as warm as it should have been, the fuss and bother had taken time and now the water was definitely chilly. Monica was heaved back into the wheelchair, naked and shivering, while hot water was added and the temperature reached a comfortable degree. At last she could relax in the warm and comfortable water.

Doreen's companion, a second year nurse by the name of Chester, was by now ignoring her apart from issuing curt instructions. "Put the chair against the bath end and cover it in towels. Brake, right, now link your left arm with mine (NO Nurse your LEFT arm) behind Monica's back, put your right arm under her bottom and when I say 'three', heave her up and into the chair." It was done. Towelling Monica dry, Nurse Chester held out her hand for Monica's clean nightdress. It was still in her locker. "Go and get it," – this through clenched teeth. Doreen flew off.

At last, at long last Monica was returned to bed, warm, clean and as comfortable as possible. Doreen just wanted to run away and cry in misery and shame.

Dinner time, she cheered up a little as she ran around with meals, helping those unable to feed themselves easily, to negotiate forks and spoons. Then the bed pan round and the washing of hands and faces. This was interrupted by the arrival of a lady in a deep coma. The ward became a hive of activity, and suddenly young men in white coats were everywhere. Everyone seemed to know what they had to do – except Doreen – who was left standing uncertainly – ignored and unwanted, looking on. So, to avoid attention, she went and hid in the sluice room until things had calmed down – it seemed the safest bet.

It was at 1pm when half the staff had gone to dinner that Nurse Chester appeared, having it seemed got over her exasperation at Doreen's failures in the bathroom. "Ah!" she said, "there you are, we've just got time to do Miss Gregg before dinner and I'll need your help. Put on a gown and mask, she's in the end bed." So, saying she stomped off, pushing a loaded trolley.

A gown and mask! Whatever were they going to do? Excitement fluttered as Doreen made her way into the ward.

As soon as she rounded the screens, she smelt it. Miss Gregg, a woman perhaps in her thirties, was lying muttering to herself and gazing blankly at nothing, her toothless mouth open and dribbling. Something brown was smeared on the top sheet and was caked on her hands, Nurse Chester was washing one of her hands and as Doreen watched she slipped a loop of bandage round Miss Gregg's wrist and secured it loosely to the bed rail. The other hand was given the same treatment and Miss Gregg continued to be oblivious of what was happening and was apparently quite un-distressed. Doreen was aware of her stomach lurching, but it was when the bed covers were turned back and the stink engulfed her that she started to retch. She was quite unable to control it and clung desperately onto the foot of the bed, her eyes streaming as her body lurched and shook. Nurse Chester regarded her quizzically.

"Go to the window and take deep breaths of fresh air through your mouth," she instructed. "It happens to all of us until we have learnt to breathe through our open mouths. Sort of shut your nose off, so you can't smell."

The retching slowed and stopped and Doreen went back to the bedside. They washed and changed the inert woman and released her hands. Doreen had no idea what condition had reduced Miss Gregg to her present state, it was enough that she was here and someone had to care for her. The disgusting bedding was dropped into a bucket and the two of them returned to the sluice.

"We caught her in time, thank goodness," Nurse Chester was sluicing the stinking bedding, whilst Doreen dismantled the trolley.

"What do you mean 'in time'?" Doreen enquired.

"In time to stop her rubbing it into her hair, or eating it," was the reply.

Doreen again rushed to the window and breathed deeply.

Busy sluicing and rinsing, Nurse Chester went on, "At least she was passive today, she can be quite aggressive at times. The night nurse got bitten last week," she giggled, "that's why Miss Gregg's teeth are in her locker and not in her mouth."

"Why is she here, what is she suffering from exactly?" Doreen enquired.

"Syphilis," – a matter of fact, non-committal reply came from Nurse Chester. Doreen's world, for a moment, rocked. Syphilis! She knew next to nothing about the disease, but vague memories surfaced of her mother putting off her childhood enquiries when she asked about the notices in public lavatories advertising VD clinics. Associated words like 'sordid sexual disease' dark, obscene activities only vaguely understood and things too dreadful to be talked of in decent society drifted into her mind. Another sudden thought occurred which Doreen hardly dared to voice. "Is it – that is – is she. . ?"

"Infectious?" Nurse Chester finished the question for her. "No, not any more. Penicillin kills the organism but penicillin can't undo the damage that the naughty little spirochete has already caused. It's affected her eyes, (you realise Miss Gregg is blind do you?) – her brain, and God knows what other bits of her. Now," Nurse Chester flung the last piece of bedding into the wet laundry bin, and turned Doreen to face her – "let's look at you." Her eyes roamed over Doreen's apron. "M'm you'll do. It's three minutes to dinner time and Matron doesn't like her nurses going into the dining room with shit on their pinnies. Come on, let's eat."

As on the previous Saturday, Dad was waiting for Doreen in the car. He was smoking his pipe and reading the newspaper when she appeared at the passenger door. "Ah, there you are love. Hungry? Mum's got a chicken cooking so let's be off." He bent to start the car before taking a proper look at his daughter, and was taken aback by her general appearance when he did so. She was tired yes, but something more, shocked? Disillusioned? Defeated? – he didn't know and decided that the best thing would be to get her home to her mother and let her cope. The interior of the family car, warm, smelling of leather, pipe smoke and Dad's aftershave seemed to Doreen like a haven of sanity and respectability where she was safe. Conversation faltered and it was with mild surprise that Doreen gazed out at a town continuing with its normal everyday business, her recent experiences and the maelstrom of emotions that they had roused in her, unknown and as nothing. They turned into the familiar road and their neighbour living opposite was washing his car, something he did without fail each Saturday.

Irritation at the man's preoccupation with something as

unimportant, as trivial, as having a clean car, bubbled through Doreen. What was happening to her?

In the house her mother was busy in the kitchen. She too, was startled by Doreen's general demeanour, but her husband's warning face over Doreen's shoulder silenced her.

Conversation continued to flag over lunch and Doreen found it difficult to do justice to the meal and had to bite back a weary and less than gentle expostulation at her father's encouragement to "Eat up love, your mother's worked hard to produce a lovely meal." Worked hard! One healthy middle-aged woman, with all morning to do it in, had produced a meal for three in a well-equipped kitchen. God! Had they no idea, Doreen thought, in their comfortable complacent lives, of what really hard work meant? No idea what some other people had to deal with and what it took out of them physically and emotionally. How could she possibly shatter their innocence and composure and did she want to anyway? She felt old and world weary and certainly impatient with anyone, including her much loved and well-meaning parents, who were outside the world of the sick. Impatience that manifests itself in bad temper.

That afternoon, Doreen, at the instigation of her mother, went upstairs and sank into her soft clean bed, blotted out her life away from this house, and slept. Dad woke her with a cup of tea at 5pm with the suggestion that they all go to the local cinema where a well-reviewed film was showing. There for a while Doreen lost herself in the exciting story, the beautiful women and handsome men of the silver screen – until – when the Prince and his Princess rode through the cheering crowd and the camera swung onto a toothless blind old woman begging for alms, the image of Miss Gregg came floating back.

It says much to record that Doreen returned to Albert Terrace the following evening to the nurse's post mortems on her and her colleagues experiences the previous day. She told them of Monica (laughter at the vision of the two of them sprawled on the floor) and she told them of Miss Gregg. Ughs and various ugh-like sounds. Interest in the art of mouth breathing, admiration for Doreen's victory over her rebellious stomach, pity for anyone reduced to such an appalling existence. Life went on.

The beginning of the end of time in the PTS. Christmas was looming and the thought of the week's pending holiday gleaming like a light at the end of a dark tunnel, growing brighter as the days went by. For some, like Theresa and Eileen, it glowed with the anticipation of a special pleasure, a special relief, its promise to be recalled and fed upon in quiet moments, but for the rest it represented – along with payday – a fast approaching goal that would mark the end of life in Albert Terrace.

But, before this goal could be reached, hanging like a grey cloud before them all was the PTS exam. It was odd really, that the nurses knew so little about this coming test. That it existed they knew and that references had occasionally been made over the last few weeks to its successful completion, but what form it would take – a practical, written, or oral exam, its duration and its pass mark were unknown. To some, who had left school at 14 without even taking any exam more onerous than an end-of-week spelling or mental arithmetic test, it held the dread of being expected to produce long discoursive written answers. To others having, possibly, to demonstrate practical ability under the critical eye of an examiner was nerve-wracking indeed. What was a pass mark and could one re-take if the worst happened?

Margery was beginning to think that perhaps the Murphy girls were right and everyone would be successful, and that further training and observation to bring the less able students up to the mark would be established in the next year, enabling them to reach a satisfactory level of practice and of exam technique in time for the first national (outside) exam in twelve months' time.

Perhaps a more solid hint that 100% pass rate was expected, lay in the allocating of bedrooms for occupation in the nurses home at the hospital when the girls returned from their Christmas break. That and the instruction for each to make themselves an appointment (during their off-duty time) with the sewing room staff – to be measured for their bespoke uniforms.

When the time came, eventually, for the exam to happen, it proved to be three, two hour papers. One each on anatomy and physiology, nursing practice and something called 'Background to Disease'. Still no pass mark identified. No practical exam and no one-to-one questions, produced relief for some, but questions in the final paper asking candidates to 'discuss' a topic, to 'evaluate' or to 'comment' produced real difficulty for those unused to presenting their opinions alongside their knowledge – and in writing! What makes a good nurse? To some die-hards of the old school, it meant someone who obeyed instructions quickly and efficiently without resorting to any questions and who abided by the rules and priorities of whichever ward sister was in charge. If these criteria were strictly followed, all of which, it was argued, had patient welfare at heart, then the ward would run smoothly and the outcome for all concerned would be success. For nurses to have opinions and make critical observations, or indeed to 'comment' on what they were expected to do, was unnecessary and quite superfluous.

Sister Lumsden, in delivering her 'Health and Disease' lectures, had encouraged debate, interaction and spontaneous contribution, as well as supplying the facts on which to base these observations. Now here was the manifestation of her efforts appearing in an exam paper. Things were a-changing and not just the advent of the new 'hard-ware' that the State through the National Health Service was providing.

The curriculum for nurse training had remained static for years – a war tends to concentrate the mind on immediate needs – and many skills, long out-dated, remained on the list of 'must knows' to be taught and assimilated. The application of leeches for the relief of congestion, the hand sewing of many-tailed bandages to be used following abdominal surgery, similarly the making of padded splints and the intricacies of bi-manual bandaging. Now perhaps these things would be swept away along with the nurse as a biddable automaton, hand maiden to other senior professionals; and along might come a more thinking, innovative, self-assertive individual whose skills might follow the whys and wherefores of her profession as well as its demands. Was this part of the exciting new concept promised by Matron eight long weeks ago?

With the exam behind them, all that remained of their PTS days was the giddy camaraderie of their last evening together – then payday – packing up every trace of their occupation of Albert Terrace – and holiday.

The usual practice at Christmas, Sister Lumsden explained, was for everyone to buy one present, put them all together, and then each claim one. What a good idea, if only they had known about this earlier. . . two people had to submit promissory notes, as they were, until tomorrow, penniless, but Margery got a hyacinth bulb in a pot, which pleased her greatly, Anne a bag of home made peppermint humbugs, and Kathleen, four hair slides with glittery glass jewels attached – just right for the Tower Ballroom at Blackpool.

Shortly after the last payday, four weeks ago, Margaret had anticipated the need for the group to mark the end of PTS, and Christmas of course, by producing a gift for Sister Lumsden and for Anne. To this end she had collected contributions from her colleagues towards the purchase of two presents, a silk scarf and some hand cream for the tutor and bath salts and soap for Anne. Both presents were received with surprised delight, and Sister Lumsden reciprocated with three bottles of white wine. The kitchen sent over a cake and some sandwiches, the fire blazed warmth and the radio did its best with light music. The nurses giggled, they danced, ate, drank, laughed and solemnly swore eternal friendship with each other, until one by one they tumbled into bed.

Next year, that is, in eight days' time, they hoped to be proper nurses, would soon have proper uniforms, and be struggling with the exhaustion and interest of a different life. Then it would be "Hello" to 1949 – and the future.

Chapter Five

"Call at Home Sister's office, before 8pm on January 2nd, and she will give you the key to your room." Positively Sister Lumsden's last direction before she wished them all a happy Christmas and retired to bed.

The following morning there was a frantic packing up of possessions, as every trace of their eight week occupation of Albert Terrace was erased, and the various buses and trains were sought that would take the nurses home for Christmas, December's salary safely in their pockets.

Kathleen O'Connor, of course, was not by choice, going home, but she departed for her room at the hospital with as much pleasure as the rest, contemplating mornings in bed, afternoons spent at a leisurely toilet and evenings in the company of her boyfriend at a variety of social goings-on. He had a wide circle of friends and possibly there would be an introduction to the flat which he shared with another young man. Imagination jiggled with delicious uncertainty at this latter possibility and what it might entail. The anticipation was exciting, the future full of promise.

When January 2nd arrived it was Anne Manning who was the first to claim her room key. The offer of a lift to Merton by a friend of her fathers had, considering the heap of luggage she

65

wished to transport, been too good to miss. The holiday had been fine, home cooking, the easing of routine and discipline, the worry of exams receding. Anne, like others, had found some difficulty in sliding back into the easy companionship of her erstwhile contemporaries; she had moved on, and so had they, the life common to them all had shifted and Anne once or twice found herself wishing to be back and enjoying the easy fellowship she had experienced at Albert Terrace. Still she was back now, and soon the rest would be arriving and the banter and noise, the highs the lows and the chatter would re-commence.

The group were to be found rooms together in what was officially known as 'Home Corridor', but was always referred to by all as 'Slum Alley'. In this very hierarchical society in which they lived, nurses were allocated rooms befitting their status – hence Slum Alley for the very newest starting ward work. The rooms weren't slums of course, they sparkled with cleanliness and were (oh! Blessed condition) centrally heated. During the 1930s, when Merton was designated as a voluntary hospital dependent for its existence on funding from benefactors' endowments and so on, a programme of refurbishment of the nurses' rooms was undertaken, as and when money was available. 1939 had stopped this enterprise and Slum Alley remained as it had been for many years.

Anne opened her door with some anticipation. A room of one's own – that locked! Inside, a narrow iron bedstead held her allocated bedding. A vast wardrobe with a drawer at the bottom would probably have held the entire clothing complement of half a dozen nurses; one upright wooden chair; an old marble topped washstand, minus its pottery artefacts, served as a dressing table – or was it meant to be a desk? There was no mirror. . . Anne viewed the cupboard under the wash stand doubtfully. What was it meant for? Surely, surely, chamber pots weren't part of the accoutrements? But no, on investigation the cupboard was empty, presumably the 'usual offices' were down the corridor, as there was no hand basin here. A high curtained window looked out, at this time of night, onto blackness, a faint line of lights showing where the main road wound its way through the neighbourhood.

Footsteps outside and one by one the nurses returned, bursting after their holiday, with life and vigour. By 8.30pm all but the two Irish girls were back, Kathleen O'Connor returned at 10.30pm, happy that her week as the sole occupant of Slum Alley was over, but of Theresa there was no sign. Margery, aware of how severely her room mate had suffered from home sickness, feared that a return to Ireland had convinced the girl that life in England was not for her. A couple of days later she was proved right. On enquiry Home Sister told them there had been a phone call, and that Nurse McCall would not be returning. Margery felt sad about this. Many times they had lain side by side in their two beds and Theresa had talked of her life on the farm – the work, the pleasures, her whole existence as one of a very large family. In fact, Margery thought, if she concentrated she could possibly name all thirteen of Theresa's siblings. She knew how her parents had met and married within one week, brought together by the local matchmaker, how the constant labour of a largely self sufficient lifestyle was shared by all the children according to their ages and capabilities, from cutting turf to turning the butter churn. She knew of the daily baking of sufficient soda bread to feed a family of sixteen and three hired men (sliced shop bread being a Sunday treat) and the occasional pig killing followed by salting, drying and rendering. Margery's own family life with parents and one brother living in a suburban semi seemed dull in comparison, but nevertheless she had taken Theresa home a couple of times on a Sunday and had been surprised at her friend's reaction. The first English home (and protestant to boot!) that Theresa had entered, it represented luxury and sophistication to be dreamed of. An electric cooker, fridge and vacuum cleaner. Amazing! And one's very own telephone! Wow! Now Theresa was back in her beloved Ireland and had presumably disappeared forever. Two lives, brought together by chance, had grown in intimacy – each enriching, for that short period, the other. Now gone, finished, an episode along the way.

Anne woke next morning at the usual "Half past six, Nurse", the click of the light switch and the sound of shovelling outside her window. She was stiff and achy. God! But that mattress was uncomfortable. It sort of crunched and rustled when one turned over – surely it wasn't made of straw. It was certainly unlike any she'd seen, or felt, before. Horse hair perhaps. She stumbled sleepily to the window and drew back the curtains. In the faint light of approaching dawn dimly lit buildings were coming to life and a few individuals were obviously preparing for a day's work.

Dominating the whole and partially obscuring the general outlook was a massive heap of coke, perhaps two or three yards from her window – no wonder the outlook had been black the previous evening. A young man in a boiler suit was shovelling coke into a wheelbarrow and transferring it into the adjacent building – presumably to feed the furnace that heated the boiler, that drove the pump that pushed the water, that filled the radiators. No – not to make the house that Jack built, but to keep the whole building warm and supply copious amounts of hot water in taps!

Anne wondered if this was the end of the night shift or the beginning of the day's work. Here was the armpit of the hospital where its essential unglamorous functions were looked after, as important, in fact, as any medical skills.

The young man with the wheelbarrow caught her eye and gave a wave. Anne, conscious of her dishevelled hair and pink spotted pyjamas returned his acknowledgement, re-drew the curtains and put on her uniform. Another beginning.

The girls knew that they were to return to the wards on which they had spent the Saturday mornings of December, an arrangement that pleased generally on the principle of 'better the devil you know'. The usual practice was for students to stay on a ward for three months before moving to acquire different experience elsewhere, but each morning at breakfast Night Sister read out duty changes over and above the three month cycle to accommodate wards experiencing a heavy work load. This sounded all right in theory, but it usually meant robbing Peter to pay Paul and disrupted nurses' work patterns. Not a popular practice.

Doreen returned to Jenner Ward with the knowledge that Miss Greg was no longer there. She had died suddenly and the relief that Doreen felt left her with much uncomfortable mind searching. What kind of a nurse was she that felt glad that a patient had died, primarily because she, Doreen, would never again have to cope with her. She decided that her emotional survival would depend on her ability to do what was presented and not consider too deeply the underlying ethics and morals of her own reactions.

Jane Kirkham and Margaret Woods both went again to Children's Ward. A few of the patients that they had known were still in residence and could be greeted like old friends.

A large department, it took up the whole of the third floor and consisted of the general ward – fifteen small beds facing fifteen cots. Then there was the nursery; another six cots for babies under twelve months old and an isolation ward with five beds or cots moved in and out as necessary.

It amazed Jane how differently children behaved, in the face of incapacity, to similarly incapacitated adults. Here was no fear of the consequences of movement, no adopting of the sick role, no dwelling on their own condition, no fear for their future progress.

In the centre of the ward a large square of carpet was scattered with toys, and bedside lockers overflowed with them. It was as if the need for tidiness and order, so beloved of some ward sisters had here been abandoned in the face of children's ability to be messy. Messy it was, for the small patients, and it was hoped they were comfortable in these strange surroundings.

A small girl, one arm and one leg in plaster, fussed over the contents of a doll's pram, pushing it with difficulty the length of the carpet, then overbalancing she got up and tried again. If these kids felt well enough to take an interest in play things – they played. If not they watched and waited until they could join in. Simple.

Routines so rigidly adhered to in many adult wards, here were relaxed. Beds were made, re-made, and changed as and when necessary, hands and faces similarly washed on the same principle, and it was appreciated that when a child 'wanted to go', he wanted to go now – not at the next appropriate time! Jane loved it on Children's Ward. The work was no less exhausting as on the other wards, but the variety tremendous. From tiny babies with perhaps, birth defects, to young teenagers with conditions that mirrored in many respects adult infirmities – medical, surgical and specialist. Just those with eye, ear, nose and throat defects didn't arrive on Children's Ward as these were catered for elsewhere, so, without a designated paediatrician to oversee the lot, anything up to ten consultants, each with their own registrar and house man, were liable to arrive to see individual patients at any time. The consultant's ward round, that ritual which demanded a metaphorical red carpet, complete silence, no smoking, scrupulous tidiness and a formal procession led by the man himself, was not the practice here.

There were very few long term patients on Children's Ward. As

69

soon as a manageable plateau was reached in a child's condition, even for those sadly incurable, they were passed on either to nurse at home or to the very very few establishments that catered for such children. These few specialist units were often so far distant from the home town that their access presented insuperable difficulty.

There was one long term resident that Jane was to meet shortly. Barbara Bouncy, aged four years, had occupied the end cot in the ward now for nearly two years. She had seen scores of student nurses come and go, dozens of junior doctors. She knew the ward routine, like no other. She could talk the medical talk, and she lay, propped up by many pillows, a little queen surveying her realm and people.

Barbara, as a normal bright two year old, had been pottering in and out of the house on a sunny afternoon. Mum busy in the kitchen, Dad tinkering with his car on the short drive in front of the house, the garden gate firmly shut. Then, not aware that his little daughter had squatted down with her doll behind the car, Dad released the hand brake to allow the car to roll back a couple of yards. Barbara's injuries were horrendous, and it was thought for some time that she would not survive, but survive she did with two broken legs and fractured pelvis and internal injuries that presented greater difficulties than the broken bones. Over the weeks that followed, if there was an infection to be caught, Barbara caught it, each time becoming very ill. It became necessary to remove a damaged kidney, to repair a perforated gut, her life went from crises to crises.

In the first few frantic weeks the parents blamed each other for the accident and as time went by the blame turned to bitter rancour. They split up, each visiting the little girl at different times, along with the relevant grandparents, aunts and uncles. They vied with each other in bringing Barbara bigger and better toys, clothes and food, and the little girl, living a life of continual discomfort and pain, became querulous, demanding and manipulative. If another child showed the slightest interest in one of her possessions she screamed for Sister. Only Sister could offer food or it was thrown in the face of the unfortunate nurse serving it. She watched the nurses, especially the newer ones, for small breaches in their working practice and 'told Sister', she whined and complained if she didn't get instant reaction to her every

70

demand and she sneered and spat at anyone who displeased her. In short she became a thoroughly objectionable child, a spoilt brat of the worst kind, difficult to handle and impossible to like. How could anyone feel such gut-wrenching compassion for this troubled child and dislike her? For many, many, nurses over the months this troubled and tormented them.

When Jane approached Barbara's cot to sit her up more comfortably to eat her dinner, she received a searching penetrating stare from Barbara's blue eyes. "I don't like you, you're fat," announced the child.

"I don't like you, either, you're rude," Jane answered mildly.

This was received in silence.

Jane approached later with a plate of dinner.

"I'm not eating that – it's horrible," was the reaction.

Jane sat down at the side of the bed. "Good, then I'll have it," she said, lifting a fork to her mouth.

This produced, "Sister, Sister, she's eating my dinner." Screams and bellows brought Sister, who was presiding over the dinner wagon, to her side.

"Enough, Barbara, do you want this dinner or not?" Sister had been through this display before.

"I'll eat it if you feed me, and you put tomato sauce on it," – this through lowered lashes and in her 'poor little girl voice'.

"When I have finished serving everyone else, I will come and see if you've eaten it. If you haven't, I will feed you then. OK?"

Barbara pouted, sulked and covered her face with the sheet a muffled, "No, now," coming from beneath.

Was Sister being unduly strict, unfeeling, lacking in compassion toward this poor child, who had suffered so much, and was still suffering in more ways than anyone could possibly know. Or was her attitude the correct one? Jane didn't know, how would she ever know? The words of a Sunday school teacher from many years ago came back to her. "We must all try to love one another, all the time, which is very hard when we don't even like each other very much. We must love the person and hate the behaviour." Jane hadn't understood the words at the time, perhaps now she did – a bit. Didn't the manifestation of love sometimes transcend what was demanded to offer what was needed? Jane gave up struggling with such difficult questions and the emotions they engendered, cleared up the dinner pots, washed sticky hands and faces and sat several bottoms on a row of potties in the bathroom. Then she had a quick smoke behind the door and got on with the job.

While Jane was wresting with her sticky problems, both ethical and literal, Margaret Woods had been directed to the Isolation Ward. It seemed something of a misnomer to Margaret as there was no special anti-infection measures taken there. Staff came in and out as necessary, wearing their usual uniforms. The five small patients were isolated from the rest of the ward and perhaps that was all that was necessary. The five little ones lay in various stages of consciousness and their care fully occupied Margaret's and a second year nurse's time. All had to be fed two hourly, three of them through gastric tubes. Bed and nappies changed, pressure and friction areas treated, observations made and recorded, fluid balance charted (that is – the weight of a dry nappy deducted from the weight of a wet one). All five of these patients were victims of the universal and very prevalent scourge of TB. In their cases all were suffering from Tubercular Meningitis. But now, Margaret was told, there was hope. A new antibiotic called Streptomycin was becoming available, its effect more specific than the widely used penicillin – and Streptomycin cured TB! Hallelujah! It was carefully injected every four hours with, Margaret learnt, every hope that the children would make a full recovery of sorts. The words 'of sorts' were ominous, for in the early days of its use 'strep' as it was soon called, whilst effective used against the TB bacillus caused damage to the eighth cranial nerve, leaving the patient deaf – sometimes completely so. A living but profoundly deaf child was surely better than a dead one. . .

That night, at her prayers, Margaret gave thanks for Streptomycin, but added a rider. "If perhaps, Lord, you could see your way to refining it or adjusting it somehow to stop it causing deafness, that would be very helpful. Thank you. Amen."

At the end of the day, Doreen and Kath from Jenner Ward, Margery and Anne from the two women's surgical wards, Lister and Fleming, Jane and Margaret from 'kids' and Audrey and Eileen from the two men's surgical wards, Brown and Raynor, stumbled back to Slum Alley an exhausted heap of young women – crumpled and stained aprons, caps awry, make-up long rubbed away, ankles swelling and desperate for a rest. One full working day. Then tomorrow, tomorrow and tomorrow. Until they got through the impact of a change from sedentary to physical work, plus the emotional battering that came along the way, they could only cope with work and bed. Audrey showed the others how to push something (a drawer from a dressing table was good, she said, except that their ancient washstands had no drawers) under the foot of the mattress to heighten it – thus helping to reduce swollen feet and ankles in time for tomorrow when the whole process would begin again.

The nurses worked a forty-eight hour week from 7.30am till 8pm with, during those hours, a 3 hour break either from 10am to 1pm, 2pm till 5pm or 5pm till 8pm. At this stage of their career the 3 hour break was, in most cases spent on their beds, gathering strength for the next shift.

Gradually the group adjusted, and decided that there was a life outside the hospital, and that it needn't always control their existence to the exclusion of everything else, and that these split hours had their advantages. An afternoon free to shop, perhaps mornings at the municipal swimming pool and (when summer came) afternoons in the park; perhaps a game of tennis or for those wealthy enough to own a set of clubs, a round of golf. Always, always, though, there was someone to do these things alongside you. Now the closed circle of Albert Terrace was widening to include others with whom one worked, and life was never lonely, communal living bringing its rewards as well as the trials for those who valued privacy above all things.

An added advantage at this time was that classroom work had been temporarily abandoned to give the new nurses a chance to adjust to ward work and to enjoy their off-duty time as they pleased, without the encumbrance of having to present oneself for a lecture on one's day off.

One by one the hated blue dresses were being discarded in favour of a made-to-measure blue and white striped dress – that fitted! Away went the caps embellished with the letters PTS, and the dresses, all sent to be laundered, mended and parcelled up ready to garb the backs of the next set of young hopefuls.

By the end of January when weekly lectures started, the group were beginning to consider themselves old hands. Sister Lumsden, busy preparing for the imminent arrival of another PTS, was nowhere to be seen and it was Miss Bailey-Scott who took charge of their continued education with more advanced

d

nursing techniques. They practised sticking hypodermic needles into oranges, the most easily obtainable object having skin and flesh similar to that of humans. They, in theory, gave stomach and bladder washouts, took blood pressures, passed catheters, prepared poultices and inhalations and started on the ubiquitous business of how to lay a trolley. To lay a trolley for a doctor to perform a variety of minor operations on the ward, and not to have it complete and with everything to hand was a sin of the deepest dye. Sadly it happened, even in those first few weeks on the wards, that one was required to perform some relatively simple procedure before one had been taught it in school, or indeed, had it demonstrated on the ward; required to do it because there was no one else available – not a happy state of affairs, and one that scared any student nurse of sensitivity to death, and may well have scared the patients similarly if they had realised the ineptitude and nervousness of their attendants.

Such an occasion almost caused Margery Harvey to be the fourth member of the group to decide to abandon their chosen career, say "not for me, thank you" and move off to pastures new. Still working on Lister Ward, Margery, a third year student called Henderson and the ward sister were the staff complement for the evening. Nurse Henderson was to work on till 10pm, when the night nurse took over, Margery and the ward sister finishing at 8pm. It had been 'operation day' and there were still several patients in a state of semi consciousness following surgery, and in addition it was Lister Ward's turn to receive any emergencies that may come in, a system by which the two consultants received onto 'their' wards on alternative weeks, any admissions deemed to be necessary.

The difficulty this particular evening was that Nurse Henderson was obviously unwell, so just before 7.30pm Sister took her temperature and found it to be very high. She sent her off to report to Home Sister, with a "You may be infectious, Nurse."

Margery laboured on, trying to do two people's work, while Sister stayed in her office to complete the day report. At 8pm she emerged and announced that Margery would have to stay on till 10pm and that Night Sister was available, if she needed her. With that she put out the night-time drugs for Margery to dispense – and left.

Margery felt sick with apprehension. She was being left in

charge of twenty patients, some very ill and hardly conscious, and with the possibility of anything coming through the door at any minute. There were still routine jobs to be done. The day's complement of face masks to wash and put to dry, flowers to be taken out, crockery to be collected in, dirty laundry piling up and needing sluicing before it could be confined to the wet laundry bin – and these were only 'things'. More importantly patients all needed settling for the night; bed pans, water jugs, bed adjustments, extra pillows. . . Had Nurse Henderson given the four-hourly penicillin injections and medicines at 6pm – or had she been too ill? Margery had no idea. There were three patients on intravenous drips, one bottle almost empty. How did you replace a bottle? Was another needed? Perhaps the day report would say. Run to the office to read it and on the way reverse to go to the aid of an old lady confused and disorientated who had removed her nightie and was attempting on frail legs to climb out of bed, naked but determined. Lifting her bodily back between the sheets, Margery thought perhaps a sedative might be prescribed for her amongst those left by Sister – she must get them out to her and to others. That bloody drip was going to empty any minute now and Margery knew that leaving an empty bottle dangling might jeopardise the whole system which would mean re-inserting it – she closed the screw on the still full tubing and left it. A woman who earlier in the day had had abdominal surgery was vomiting into her pillow and whimpering as the heaving of her body pulled on the newly inserted stitches. Margery cleaned her up and promised some pain relief, checked unconscious patients, breathing, took another lady off her bed pan (half an hour I've been waiting, Nurse!) and sped to the office to investigate the drugs left for distribution. On the way, the phone rang and Margery felt her bladder give way. Please God, please God don't let it be an emergency, she prayed frantically. The phone, when she got to it, went dead.

She examined the tray of drugs. A dozen or so teaspoons were laid out, the name of the patient and the drug tucked on a scrap of paper under each, the tablets in the bowl of the spoon. Sodium Amytal, Soneryl, Codein, and on three labels 'Morphia' – tiny white tablets that looked like Saccharines. Margery considered. She had thought that Morphia was given by injection but these were tablets. Perhaps Morphia could be taken by mouth too. She carried the tray around, sitting patients up, finding water, helping them swallow that which hopefully might bring some comfort. Just as she gave out the last tablet, Night Sister arrived to do her first round of the night, surprised to find someone as inexperienced as Margery alone. She read the day report, noted the entry of Morphia in the Dangerous Drugs Book and presumed that this had been given by the day sister. She changed the empty bottle on the drip that had caused Margery such misgivings, checked operation sites, aspirated Ryles Tubes, examined drips to see that needles were still running into veins and not tissues, then helped Margery to fix cot sides onto the bed of the confused escapee, and turned off the lights, then leaving her office number on the desk, she continued her journey round the hospital.

At ten to ten the phone rang again, this time telling Margery that a patient with an acute abdomen would be arriving shortly and was to be prepared for theatre. Margery turned down one of the two empty beds in the ward and found the admissions book. This time she prayed that the night nurse would arrive before the new patient. She didn't know what 'preparing for theatre meant' and doubted her ability to deal with a frightened woman in pain or cope with the worried relative probably with her – when she herself was frightened and worried and out of her depth.

The night nurse arrived! Resigned to what she knew was going to be an eventful night. She was coming to the end of the three months of night duty in this her third year of training, and the next ten hours, mostly spent working alone, she knew were going to be busy. She dismissed Margery and settled down to read the day report. It really wasn't fair, she thought, to come on duty and to find the ward in such disorder, not fair to have left a kid on her own to manage what was obviously beyond her, and not fair, most importantly, to patients who trusted that their care would be efficiently and willingly carried out by knowledgeable staff. And now she must get round to each patient before the new one arrived and commanded her attention.

When Margery left the ward reaction set in and she began to shake. Then nausea swept over her and she bolted into the nearest toilet and vomited. It occurred to her then, that she'd not had her evening meal so she went down to the kitchens and begged a sandwich. Thus armed she found her room, dropped into bed, munched her bread and cheese and had a drink of cold water. There were tea making facilities along the corridor but they were just too onerous to contemplate, and anyway her sugar ration was in the dining room now, closed and dark. She slept.

The morning after, Margery read in the night report that a Mrs Middleton had been admitted at 10.15pm the previous night with a burst appendix, and was now recovering with the threat of peritonitis still present. In the daylight, and with colleagues around her, Margery's experiences of the previous evening were fading slightly and feelings of indignation that she had been put in such a situation were arising. At 10am she went off duty for three hours and joined Kathleen, who was on her day off and still in bed, and Jane, also having a morning off duty, in Kathleen's room for a gossip.

Did they know, Margery asked, that you could swallow Morphia as well as inject it? No, they didn't. "You can't," said Kathleen, "it doesn't work orally, it's got to get into the bloodstream." She'd seen the staff nurse put the little tablet, with a drop or two of water, into the bowl of a teaspoon and dissolve it over a spirit burner, then draw it up into the syringe and inject it.

"Oh, lordy, lordy," Margery clutched her head. "I gave it out and made them swallow it."

"So what? You weren't to know," they both agreed.

"No, but three people suffered a miserable night of, at least, discomfort because of my ignorance" Margery wailed.

Could she live with the possibility of another evening like last night, and during such an evening make even worse and possibly far-reaching mistakes? At the moment she thought not, but if she threw in the towel now because of that possibility the last three months of the life she had begun to accept as hers, would be lost. Why was life and its decisions so hard? Could she ever be satisfied with life as perhaps – a typist? But would she ever have the knowledge and capability to be responsible for running a ward? – and be confident in doing so? It seemed there was a long way to go – she would just have to keep struggling inwardly, and outwardly adopt a more confident demeanour to reassure patients. Be like a swan, she thought, outwardly serene, confident and in command. But paddling like mad where it can't be seen.

It wasn't as if there was anyone to talk these things over with, except one's contemporaries of course. Parents were too remote from any concept of what was entailed and too emotionally connected to be of practical help. The thought of approaching Miss Bailey-Scott, supposedly the students guide and mentor, was untenable. To talk to Matron would mean confessing her ineptitude and her mistake with the Morphia and might get her the sack and oh! The ignominy of that. Meanwhile the ward was one member of staff short.

Nurse Henderson was found to be suffering from infective hepatitis and would be off sick for some time. Two weeks in bed under the care of Home Sister, two weeks at home recuperating was the usual routine. Infective hepatitis was something that most establishments having communal eating arrangements found cropped up from time to time. Nurse Henderson would not now be able to take her finals with the rest of her colleagues. The General Nursing Council, who laid down the rules for training periods, decreed that a total of 3 weeks sick leave in three years was the maximum allowed. Anyone having more than three weeks must extend their training by three months or more and take their finals at its completion.

Lister Ward's meagre staffing levels were getting sparser. Everyone was having to work unpaid overtime to keep the ward covered. It was expected and accepted. After all, more bodies could not be manufactured out of thin air, or taken from stock. Nurses were there to nurse and must expect the rough with the smooth. It just seemed, at times, that 'the rough' happened too frequently for comfort.

Chapter Six

Valentine's Day! Jingle bells, artificial snow and the present buying frenzy of Christmas long gone, the chickens, eggs, and gambling lambs of Easter still to come, so the good businessmen of Merton were squeezing what they could from the romantic expectations of February 14th. Shop windows danced with flowers and pink fluffy hearts – lu-rve was in the air. Anne, having brought a patient's discarded newspaper back to the nurses' home with her at supper time, saw the advert, it said: 'Come and find your Valentine at our grand celebratory dance. Public Hall, 7pm till 12am bar, refreshments, Les Marsden and his band, late buses 12.30am. Tickets three and sixpence.' How could it be resisted? Anne and Audrey had the evening off, Margery would come back early from her day off, Doreen and Jane were working till 8pm but could be ready by 8.30pm. They would have a taxi! Coming home they would leave to chance. Maybe 'walked home' by the new and exciting valentines they were bound to meet – or the bus? Two taxis in one evening was an extravagance too far to contemplate.

Slum Alley bustled with preparations. Hair washing, nail varnishing, arm pit shaving, dress ironing and the borrowing and swopping of their combined wardrobes. Doreen's necklace went with Margery's dress; her precious nylons were brought out and examined anxiously for ladders, Anne hadn't any suitable shoes, but Audrey had a spare pair that fitted. In and out of each other's rooms they went until everyone had achieved their most glamorous selves. They signed themselves 'in' to satisfy Night Sister's regular perusal, and climbed grandly into their taxi. The austere Public Hall built for, and largely used for, large meetings and concerts had done its best with fairy lights round the door. Inside there were heart shaped balloons and pink streamers, staff with flowers in their hair or button holes and NOISE. Every dance hall, and there were four in Merton, had its own or a visiting dance band, semi-professionals adept on saxophone, drums or keyboard playing a repertoire of popular dance tunes, mostly from Hollywood via the film industry. Public Hall dances were definitely at the upper end of respectability, others went down hill, like the town centre pubs, from 'posh' to 'grotty' depending not so much on the premises as on the clientele. To each his own.

To say that the nurses enjoyed themselves was an understatement. Work hard play hard, and as soon as it leaked out that the five were student nurses, their popularity was ensured. Why young men find nurses so attractive remained a mystery to the girls. They knew each other so well – they weren't prettier, more generous with their sexual favours, better dressed, more intelligent, more fun to be with, than anyone else, but none of them had difficulty in attracting male attention.

"They want a nanny-figure – poor sods," was Audrey's opinion, but she still went off with her current 'poor sod' and ate and drank at his expense.

Anne, quick-stepping across the expanse of polished floor felt that the young man in whose arms she danced was familiar, but she couldn't place the time or occasion when they might have met, and dismissed the thought as imagination. Then, swinging her expertly round a corner as the saxophone blared the latest tune he asked pleasantly, "And do you still wear pink spotted pyjamas?"

Anne's mouth fell open in surprise. How could he – ? Who was he – ? Then the penny dropped – he was the young man who shovelled coke outside her window, now looking clean and presentable. "Of course I do," she replied without missing a beat. "You've recognised me with my clothes on, but I didn't recognise you with a clean face!"

He was, it seemed, a medical student earning some money

where and when he could, which was why his coke-shovelling activities were irregular, a job 'found' for him by his dad who delivered the coke that kept them all warm.

At midnight the last waltz found all the girls with a partner to walk them back to the hospital, possibly half a mile distant. Long enough for hand holding, a bit of a cuddle and a goodnight kiss. And getting back to their rooms? Officially of course, as far as Night Sister was concerned, they were already 'in', and by now tucked up asleep. But a hospital never closes. The doors are always open to receive the sick and the injured and especially on a Saturday night, the daft the drunk and the disorderly. Plenty of opportunity for five extra bodies to walk in, find their beds and get at least a modicum of sleep before the light clicked on with "Half-past six, Nurse."

Kathleen was worried. Sort of. Worried, excited, awe struck and curious. How could you possibly be all those things at once: In truth, she had enjoyed a wonderful Christmas that had left her fulfilled and happy. Matthew was all she had ever wanted in a man and their association had grown and deepened. The trouble was that with all the practical changes in her life that starting full-time work on the wards had brought, it had been early February before she realised that her mid-January period had never arrived. Now it was March and February had passed with still no monthly evidence. . . and her bra was getting very tight.

Kathleen wasn't daft and the thought that she had a bit of Matthew inside her growing a-pace, thrilled her. She felt slightly nervous about breaking the news to him about their probable impending parenthood, because though he had told her that he loved her many times, there had never been any mention of a ring or promise for the future, nor indeed, had she ever sought any.

She thought vaguely about getting some medical confirmation of her condition before breaking the news, but how? When the nurses had arrived last October they had been required to change their doctors to one of the two part-time consultant physicians employed by the hospital, both of whom also ran general practices. Any consultation with her registered GP therefore could only be accessed through the home sister. Kathleen didn't even know where 'her' doctor held his surgery, and to request a consultation via the home sister would inevitably raise the question, "Why?" The consequences of her answer would, Kathleen was sure, result in dismissal. Surrounded as she was by medical gentlemen of all shapes and sizes, the idea that she might way-lay one, pass him a rubber glove, and suggest they retire to a side ward for a quick examination of her cervix, she dismissed as ridiculous, even having a private giggle at this impossible scenario. No, time would have to be her confirmation. She would wait till next month when another few days' holiday was due, marking their first six months of training. She would pack her bags, leave a letter of resignation and not return.

Matthew received her news without any great show of emotion of any kind. He enjoyed Kathleen's company greatly and recently had begun to think that this was the real thing, not just two youngsters having a good time in every sense of the word. He had tried, and generally succeeded, in pushing these feelings away as 'not in the plan'. After all, he was 22 with a brand new degree in civil engineering and not quite one year into his 2nd year stint as a graduate learner in the local surveyor's department. Then he would have to do his National Service. . . A baby! His earning capacity for the next three years would be meagre. Where would they live. *How* would they live? Parenthood had never entered his thoughts. To do him justice, never for one moment did he consider walking away from the problem. His baby, his girlfriend – fiancé – wife. So be it.

To say that they lived happily ever after would be untrue; they lived in relative poverty in rented rooms after a quick registry office wedding. Part time shop assistant jobs for Kathleen and lonely months with a small baby whilst Matthew did his duty by King and Country and learnt to handle a rifle. His degree earned him sergeant's stripes though and they managed. Goodbye to the nursing career, which for Kathleen had only been a means to an end – the abandonment of life in Ireland with her parents.

The rest of her PTS viewed Kathleen's departure with no surprise. How could any girl live in such close proximity to others and keep her condition secret? They had watched Kathleen's expanding waistline, well camouflaged with an all-encompassing apron, with interest and curiosity, and a growing admiration for her wish for privacy regarding her personal affairs. Goodbye Kathleen – six months had gone by and the eleven were now seven.

Pastures new! A change of wards and that to which they had grown familiar left behind for new experiences. Doreen was to go to the Children's Ward and was quite excited about the prospect mainly influenced by Jane's enthusiasm. Jane herself was to go to Fleming Women's Surgical Ward and Margery to Jenner Medical Ward. Whether this would be to the women's 'end' or the male 'end' wasn't clear. Anne, allocated for the first time to a male ward, looked forward to this with anticipation; to Margery the possibility filled her with curiosity, and not a little trepidation. "It will all sort out," said Eileen, the practical, stolid, reliable worker "Take what comes and do your best."

Audrey Renton was taking Margery's place on Lister Ward and was happy to be back nursing women. Her 'Mary's' days had faded during the last 3 months in the face of her experience on a male surgical ward. Strangely she had taken little part during the last few weeks in the collective introspection, the chatter, the raking over the day's work that played such a large part in the embryo nurses' lives. She remained 'of' the group but not really 'in' it, disappearing for days off and holidays, but where and to what no one ever knew. Not unfriendly, but making no close liaisons, Audrey had become a dark horse. No one really knew of Audrey's performance bed-side. There were apparently no tales she wanted to tell to the rest. Tales that began, "On the ward today" – and went on to tell of the highs and lows, unusual happenings, what Sister said, did and how she reacted. Nothing.

Working as they did in isolation from their immediate classmates it was only through chatter in dining room and sitting room that more information might be forthcoming. Still nothing, which was surprising as in an all-female environment, where both living and working together was the norm, opinions as to the general capabilities of each other were well known. 'So and so' was good to work with, or skived at every opportunity, was reliable, careless, or a worrier. Then of course there was the ultimate accolade – 'so and so' could GET THROUGH. 'Getting through' was the ubiquitous aim of every nurse – to get the routine work (of which there was always too much) done satisfactorily and deal with anything else that happened – and happen it did – to impede one along the way. "We'll never get through," was the sometimes unspoken worry always lurking behind the day's endeavours. Everyone knew what it meant to 'get through' or not, as the case may be, but probably few could put it into words. The relentless need to accomplish too many tasks, if possible with patience and goodwill, in limited time and before the next imperative was thrust forward or the next crisis broke Audrey's ability to 'get through' was unknown.

She was, she herself felt, coping reasonably well on Lister Ward, until an incident which might be described as ridiculous, sinister, tragic or laughable depending on your outlook, but which was recounted to the rest as they all piled into one bedroom that evening, noted as Audrey's first contribution, and marked and inwardly digested for their own survival in the future.

Audrey had collected up the bunches of flowers brought by visitors and taken them into the bathroom to put into vases and distribute for their owners to admire. A beautiful bunch of red and white carnations, obviously hot house grown, stood out against the other rather nondescript offerings, so Audrey found the best of the ward's vases in which to display them, carrying them out for the lucky recipient's pleasure and that of her immediate neighbours. There was an empty bed, with locker, prepared for a casualty expected from outpatients at any time, so Audrey set the vase down there and returned to the bathroom to complete her flowery task. Audrey had lined up the filled vases on a tray to carry them out when Sister appeared at the door. She was shaking – with temper, with fear or whatever, Audrey couldn't decide, but she was holding the vase of red and white carnations so recently placed adjacent to the empty bed prepared for whatever casualty was to send them.

"Never, never, put red and white flowers together in a vase on my, or on any other, ward." Sister spoke through clenched teeth. "They are a sign of death." And with that she returned whence she had come leaving a rather bewildered Audrey to separate the flowers and mix in some leaves. When she emerged with the vases all was hustle and bustle as the new patient, a woman who had been pulled out of a burning building, had arrived and relatives, doctors, porters and police were all in evidence. "Thank goodness," Audrey thought, visiting time was over. Then she noticed that two patients were crying, and going over to see if she could help she found that it wasn't for the newcomer, who was obviously in a grievous state, but because of the red and white flowers that had appeared so briefly on the opposite side of the ward.

"It's an omen," sobbed one of the women, who had thoughtlessly conveyed her knowledge of hospital superstitions to her neighbour.

"What does one say? Or do?" asked Audrey of the rest, who gazed back blankly at a loss to know how one coped with primitive beliefs so easily roused in the alien environment of a hospital ward. A ward full of individuals made vulnerable by their own bodily weaknesses.

Margaret made a mental note to discuss it with her fiancé when she next saw him. Margery wondered about the origins of such a belief. There were usually elements of veracity in old wives' tales, but this was something more than that. Some history and ill-founded belief dating back to the Great Plague perhaps? She gave it up.

It was Eileen then that said, "Well, finish the story – there is more, isn't there?"

Audrey gulped. "She, that is the lady that got burnt, died at 6pm this evening, and I helped to lay her out – my first experience of the last offices." There was silence. Several of the group had already had this task to perform.

"You remember your first one," Eileen said, "and your most recent one. The rest blur together."

"The last service we can give – to preserve dignity in death," this from giddy Anne Manning, for once solemn. "It has to be done and to do it reverently and gently is part of what we are here for."

Nods of agreement. "And now," said Jane. "My mum has given me a box of homemade buns to bring back. Whose turn is it to make the tea, and who, may I ask, has helped themselves to my bloody sugar?"

"Men don't do pain," Anne announced. "Can't cope with it like women can." Anne, not exactly naïve when it came to the male sex, was learning a lot on Brown Ward.

"True," said Eileen, "but then women are wired to put up with labour pains, so I suppose they manage better."

"M'm, but I tell you what," went on Anne, "once men are feeling a bit better they are willing to help you, whilst women will lie back and make the most of being waited on and they don't lift a finger to help you or themselves if someone else is there, and willing."

"True," said Eileen again, "but what would you do? I'd take my ease while I could. There's still an element of chivalry buried somewhere in the male ego, and whilst our patients are not in a position to scatter rose petals beneath one's feet, they can, and do, help clear away the used breakfast crockery. Sometimes! Anyway," she went on, "from what I hear, you are the most outrageous flirt so I expect, all that can, are falling over themselves to help you."

"What," Anne expostulated, "with Sister forever looming and waiting to pounce on any signs of impropriety in her staff! No, I flirt ever so mildly with anyone over sixty."

" – Sixty!" Eileen interposed, "crikey, that's when they're most hungry."

"Sixty and sixteen – when the urge is going and when it's growing."

"Well, anyway," Anne continued, "they seem to like it and even Sister grins at my sparkling repartee. I tell you what though," now Anne was serious, "all these young men who come in with inguinal hernias. They have to lie flat for 10 days (which incidentally makes a lot of work for the likes of thee and me), but after they've got over the first day, they don't feel ill and are bored out of their minds. Nothing to do but watch us bend over and expose a length of black stockings. They even have it organised," there was indignation in Anne's tone. "Two of them in opposite beds – until I twigged it. 'Oh, Nurse Manning, darling, I seem to have dropped my book, my pencil, my lighter, my anything-at-all. Could you reach it for me?' and his friend across the ward enjoys the spectacle of me trying to reach behind his locker."

"Perhaps," Eileen said, "you could give them a treat, say once a day. Allow them a viewing then say 'no' consistently and leave the floor littered until the following day. It's called 'meeting the patients' needs'!" She roared with laughter. "Perhaps we should put it to Miss Bailey-Scott, there's a definite gap in the curriculum there!"

Anne's, romance, if it could be called that, with the coke shovelling Lothario from the Valentine's dance continued sporadically. He would pop up now and again when at his parents home in Merton, but had given up the coke routine in favour of pint-pulling at an establishment near the medical school in Manchester. He absorbed with interest Anne's hospital tales, comical, grave, gory, heartbreaking or funny but always of interest and new to him. In his first year at medical school he neither knew the inside of a hospital, nor had he ever seen a patient – that would come soon enough – but meanwhile, whilst Anne felt superior in her practical experience, he could run circles round her far from perfect appreciation of anatomy and physiology. His most useful contribution to date had been the recounting of some quite disgustingly obscene mnemonics, memory aides, for such things as 'name the bones of the face', or the 'number and functions of the cranial nerves'. Hardly lovers talk, but then they were both 18 and had all the time in the world for such things. No sweat, good friends, entertaining company and that suited them.

As the approaching few days' holiday grew nearer, anticipation as to their immediate future, slightly raised above the lowest rungs of the career ladder, jiggled in the girls' minds. A new PTS was due to start full time work on the wards so no longer were they 'the last PTS' but October '48 PTS. A new set of students was taking its first tentative steps towards initiation into full time ward routine. Wearing the same blue dresses, now a shade more faded, as those worn by their predecessors, they came with a mixture of nervousness, excitement and, for some not a little bravado, to occupy Slum Alley and meet the exhaustion of early days.

After six months service the nurses were entitled to two weeks' holiday, but as they had already 'spent' some of this at Christmas the April break was considerably reduced.

"Do you realise," said Eileen, as they all settled into their new rooms in the nurses' home proper, "because we started late October/beginning of November we are destined never to have a summer holiday for the foreseeable future? April and November for us. It's probably written on tablets of stone in the cellars of The General Nursing Council. 'Verily thou shall not take leave until thou hast laboured mightily for six months', so sayeth the Chief Nurse of Blessed Renown.

"M'm, but four weeks a year is quite generous." Margaret always saw the positive.

"A right little Pollyanna, you are," grumbled Jane. "Don't forget we never get any bank holidays. I wonder if anyone got VE day?" This received in silence. It was past and gone.

The new rooms were a big improvement on Slum Alley. Interior sprung mattresses, hot and cold running water in gleaming hand basins and not an old washstand in sight. On the second and third floors many windows looked out onto rooftops and to the hills beyond, and there was even a rather ancient lift to take you up there. The girls were no longer housed together, occupying rooms wherever there was a vacancy on one of any of the four corridors. Their tight-knit group was extending to include others that shared the same amenities – namely an electric kettle and tea and milk allocation.

Of course lectures and, in fact, all training school work were still spent together. This continued a-pace, the Scaley-Botts' lectures and demonstrations becoming more sophisticated as expertise and practice required more explicit skills. Mixed in with the factual knowledge she imparted were the ethical and behavioural standards the tutor expected, some applied psychology and her own personal experiences. Incidents that began: "When we were operating in the Malayan jungle" to illustrate dehydration and the loss of salt from the skin in extreme climates, or "The improvement in health of our native servants when we insisted on brown rather that white rice was significant." So many of the Scaley-Bott's descriptions of the symptoms, treatment and outcome of an affliction ended with the words – "I know, nurses, because I've had it," anything from amoebic dysentery to house-maid's knee, Miss Bailey-Scott seemed to have suffered it – and survived. Whether she was a hypochondriac, a fantasist or an extremely experienced guide and mentor, her students never knew. She was the Scaley-Bott-upright well informed – unique!

Now lectures too, were tempered by heads of other departments whose teaching duties came along with the position they held. There was the head pharmacist who gave all his lectures with his back to the class, muttering inaudibly whilst writing lists of drugs and their dosages on the blackboard for the class to memorise. Some hope. The micro-biologist from the laboratories, who seemed frankly bewildered at being faced with a bevy of 18–19 year old girls, unhappy away from his specimens and Petri dishes. An interesting, informative and lively lecture however, was delivered by the head physiotherapist, a lady with, if her long suffering staff were to be believed, a formidable reputation who ran her department with high expectations applied to professionals and patients alike. Whatever her practical skills entailed, this lady could certainly teach, and the nurses benefited from it. In a different vein but equally effective was the chief radiographer from the X-ray department. Evidently, it was learnt, the first X-ray department in the country, outside London, had been established in Merton. There's pioneering for you! – and there was still, this enthusiastic lady told them, exciting possibilities as yet only vaguely understood, of other 'magic machines' that could look inside a body in minute detail. She left leaving the class stimulated and informed. What a gift it is to be able to communicate effectively and promote enthusiasm in others.

Only a week to go to the April holiday and Doreen for one was hanging on to the thought like a drowning man glimpsing the shoreline. Work on Children's Ward has lived up to expectations in part, with certain exceptions which troubled her and broke into her sleep. She was tired. She carried a mind-numbing burden of tiredness that never left her, and she had had a sort of head-achy cold now for three weeks. A cold that neither developed nor resolved, but just added to her miseries. What Doreen could not bring herself to accept with calmness and firmness was the forcible holding still of distressed children whilst a colleague undertook an unpleasant or painful procedure. Procedures such as injections, wound dressing, venipuncture or lumbar puncture, had to be done, and depending on a child's age and understanding, sometimes no amount of reasoning, cajoling, cuddling or bribery would persuade a child to lie still and tolerate what was to come. Whether Doreen was holding or treating a child, the sobs screams and pleas broke her heart. She knew that there was no alternative means of treatment to offer, that it had to be done and that a needle snapped off inside a wriggling child could have unfortunate consequences. She also knew that the natural response to the certainty of immediate pain, was for a child to rebel physically and with loud protest. The protests, the screams, invaded her sleep and she woke to repeat again in reality the night-time horror of her dreams.

One more day and then holiday. "Could you give Nurse Johnson a hand in the nursery – she's got a pair of new-borns, twins, transferred from the maternity hospital that are very difficult to feed." Sister instructed as Doreen reported for duty on her last day before the holiday. Good, she thought, babies to feed. Warm milky little mouths, tight shut eyes and a chance to sit and patiently persuade them to take a proffered bottle – just what I need.

When Doreen opened the nursery door, Nurse Johnson was sitting in front of the window, her back to the room, a baby shrouded in blankets on her knee. "Hi – am I glad to see you!" she greeted Doreen. "I've got a full time job with these two and I'll be glad of a hand. This is James, David is there," she nodded at a cot in the corner. "I've set you a feed tray, so start feeding him. Six drops at a time is about all they can cope with."

Gosh, Doreen thought, they must be very small, very premature, and going over to David's cot she pulled back the sheet – then recoiled with a gasp. For a moment reality vanished and the room reeled. She held tightly to the cot rail to steady herself and forced herself to look again at the small individual in the cot. A grotesque distorted face, the like of which she had never seen before gazed back at her. Hideous, monstrous, nose and mouth one gaping hole, yet still discernable as what nature normally intended, but now twisted and malformed to the point when feeding, crying and even breathing was difficult.

Seeing Doreen's discomfiture, Nurse Johnson offered reassurance. "Hare lips and cleft palates – both of them," she said. "What a facing for the parents. They will be repaired, of course, but seeing your first one is a shock – did no one tell you?" She continued, "We've got to get enough nutrients into these scraps to make them strong enough to undergo the operation. Watch me."

With infinite care, the nurse dripped milk into the gaping hole in the little face and stroked his throat to help it down. "The danger is that they inhale it – it's a tedious business – you have a go."

Doreen lifted David. She must not, she told herself, think of this tiny, deformed person as 'it'. The child's eyes, normal, dark blue and unfocused as are all newborn baby's eyes seemed to gaze back at her, a small pink tongue waggled. This was someone's son, probably planned for, anticipated, on whom hopes had been built, dreams dreamed. Could the patient dripping of milk, a surgeon's skill, and more patient after-care allow these dreams to be fulfilled? The sight of the child still repelled Doreen, but she made herself handle and feed him in this very unnatural way – one more effort to be made in a life that seemed to her to be endless effort.

The twins had been born by caesarean section and were small but at 5lbs plus, of reasonable weight. After gently preparing the parents for the shock of seeing their sons they had been introduced to them by the obstetrician and assured of the possibility of corrective surgery. Father had been stoical if shocked, but mother had rejected her babies with hysterical weeping. Now father had an additional problem – his wife's condition. Weak from surgery, hormones awry as has every new mother, she submitted to the regular extraction of her breast milk and its transportation to Children's Ward for her babies' feeds. To move the children away from the maternity wards and their parent had been a difficult decision. Perhaps right, perhaps wrong. Only time would tell for this family and their future cohesion.

All this Nurse Johnson conveyed to Doreen whilst the two of them, sat, each with a baby on her knees, dripping breast milk into the babies, a difficult and messy business. At 9.30 her colleague went to lunch, leaving Doreen to clear away the implements and prepare for the next feed in two hours' time. When Doreen's turn to take a break came, she went to her bedroom instead of the dining room, sat on her bed and wept. She cried for the babies struggling to maintain life, for their parents, and for herself. Mostly she wept for herself. For her inability to control her own emotions. Emotions that she found so overwhelming, and for her reaction to unexpected shocks and to other people's pain. And, oh God! She was so tired. . .

After a while Miss Bailey-Scott's words came back to her 'you will want to cry, and when you have cried you will go back to work.' Doreen washed her face, combed her hair, gave her nose a good blow, and went back to the nursery. At 11 o'clock, they lifted, changed, washed, powdered and cuddled the babies, then started feeding again. The endless battle. It would be nice to record that the babies thrived. That their mother accepted them and their deformities were reversed. Maybe all that did indeed happen, but who knows? Patients of all shapes, sizes and ages come and then they go – to better or worse circumstances. Mostly it is not for the nurse working in hospital to ever know. It has to be enough that for a limited period her work helps them at a time when they are very vulnerable, frightened, perhaps 'lost'. That is a privilege and it has to be enough.

When Doreen got home for the start of her holiday, she went straight to bed. She slept all that night and till teatime the next day, when, like the first time she had arrived home exhausted, she was woken by Mum with a cup of tea and the suggestion that they all go to the cinema. There in the warmth and darkness, Doreen slept again.

She woke finally, now at home of course, at 6am the following day, achy, hungry and rather ashamed of her ability to sleep when away from the hospital. Her worried parents had, meanwhile hatched a plan. Would Doreen, with Mum, like a few days in Lytham St Annes? Sea air, possibly even a bit of early sunshine. They could walk in the re-awakening promenade gardens, browse through the shops, take morning coffee or afternoon tea at J. R. Taylors – a favourite up-market café. Yes, she would! Dad duly delivered them to a hotel facing the sea and they both dozed in deckchairs on their balcony, enjoying a feeble sun, wrapped in thick jumpers and trousers. Inexplicably Doreen's neck felt sore, and she had a troublesome 'spot' where her uniform collar had chafed. By evening it had grown into a hard lump so Doreen took some aspirin and went to bed. The next morning the swelling was much worse and swallowing was painful, so a worried mother got a taxi and took her daughter to the local hospital. There Doreen was given a light anaesthetic and the abscess, for such it was, was opened and drained. It was a pale and even more fragile daughter that Dad brought home later in the day. So much for the seaside holiday.

Mother, now even more worried regarding Doreen's well being, spoke to the family doctor who had known Doreen since babyhood, but he explained gently but firmly that she was no longer his patient and that medical ethics forbade him treating her. When the new GP, who was also the consultant that Doreen had last seen with his retinue of minions doing a ward round, arrived in her bedroom, it was quite a shock. But he was kind, fatherly and after examining his patient and taking a blood specimen, he sat on the bed and regarded her quizzically.

Are you happy in your work at the hospital?" he enquired.

Doreen looked back at him in some bewilderment. This was totally unexpected and she didn't know – had never considered – what was 'happy' – was she happy? The doctor helped her out.

"Do you ever feel carefree? Look forward eagerly and with pleasurable anticipation to what the day's work will bring?"

Doreen thought of the tense anxiety with which she met each day, the unexpected shocks that she had encountered that had left her emotionally drained, the continual dread of being asked to do something for which she was ill-equipped and that in doing it she would make a mistake which would have far reaching consequences. A mistake born of inexperience and ignorance but none the less dreadful for all that. Carefree! How could anyone be carefree surrounded by other people's suffering and loss – and when one's back, legs and shoulders were all crying out for rest.

Doreen looked back at the doctor and answered simply and truthfully. "No I don't."

"I am putting you 'off sick' for two weeks," he replied busy with his pad of certificates, "and I want you, in that time, to consider whether or not you want to continue in this particular line of work. It calls for a great deal of physical stamina and the ability to withstand continual contact with suffering. Not everyone has the ability within them to find that state of mind that allows them to care at a level that is acceptable and adequate, but also leaves intact deeper personal involvement."

All this was delivered gently, with pauses for Doreen's comments, opinions, arguments – but none came. He patted her hand, spoke to the parents, and left promising another visit with the blood test findings.

Ten years! Doreen thought. For ten years I have dreamt of being a nurse. Everyone from the grocer's boy to the headmistress at school, the St John's Ambulance Brigade Commandant, friends and relatives – all know of my intentions. Many have told me, with little basis for their belief, that I am a 'born nurse'. Huh! was there such a person? God knows, she thought, I have tried and tried. Of course there had been bright spots. The camaraderie of colleagues, the belief that her work was valued, worthwhile, the appreciation and thanks of patients recovered, the stimulations of acquiring new knowledge. But, but but, never again to go rigid with horror and shock at some unexpected disclosure. Never again to feel that heart wrenching compassion that left one weak with unanswered questions. Never to hear children screaming with pain and fright, to feel the pressure and fear that one would not 'get through', or to step onto a ward and dread what one might find or be asked to do. It would be what? A blessed release. . . There were so many things that as the weeks went by she had found a burden too heavy. Too many things incompatible with 'carefree'.

Over the next few days Doreen considered carefully. She thought objectively of the last six months and what it had meant to her, the positive and the negative. She thought of the loss of face she would suffer if she 'threw in the towel' now – the 'born nurse' given up after 6 months. She was eighteen years old and didn't know how to feel carefree. She had been in love for ten years with the image of herself as a caring compassionate knowledgeable angel in a cap and apron. Well, the compassion she had felt so strongly had proved to be too much for her. The caring was limited by pressure of work and the knowledge she had gained served more to indicate how much she didn't know, and how inadequate was her knowledge in her day-to-day work.

Sadly she composed a letter of resignation and told the truth. "I believe I have not the physical nor the emotional strength to give to my patients what they deserve and have a right to expect from their nurses. Therefore, it is with regret. . ."

Chapter Seven

"Have you seen him?" Jane joined a group of nurses in the dining room, enjoying their mid-morning break. Plonking her tea cup and the ubiquitous jam and bread down on the table, she beamed round at the group, bubbling over with her latest tit-bit of news.

"You were born about 200 years too late," Margaret grumbled. "You'd have made a good Town Crier. What is it this time – another phantom chip-range?"

Last week Jane had been bursting with the news that she had seen a large deep fat fryer being delivered to the kitchens, promising chips and battered fish to replace the steamed fish, white sauce and 'mash' that appeared every Friday. So far no chips had materialised and Jane had been teased about it ever since. A mirage in the desert of their daily diet, it was decided.

In the somewhat closed community of the hospital, largely staffed by women, it was not the life and death dramas of the wards and departments that held the nurses' interest, they happened all the time, it was the small items of gossip, information and news that captured their attention. Sister Bennett on Gynae Ward had purchased two budgerigars for the dayroom (making another task for the most junior nurse – cleaning out the bird-cage); Nurse so-and-so had been seen coming out of the local pub with the houseman from the Orthopaedic Ward; the butter ration was going to be replaced in part by margarine and so on. Each nugget of information holding a fascination for this introspective community beyond that of other people's more fundamental troubles.

"Have we seen who?" The question hung in the air.

"Doctor Anderson's new registrar," Jane replied, still hugging her news to herself.

"Two heads? Turns cartwheels up the ward for the patients' entertainment? Is engaged to Matron?"

"No," said Jane, "he's black!" This silenced them.

"Black! Do you mean from Africa?"

"How should I know where he's from?" expostulated Jane. "He has a brownish, blackish skin, black curly hair and thickish lips."

"Does he speak English?" asked Audrey.

"Seems to," said Jane. "I couldn't really hear."

This news needed some digesting. Most of the half dozen nurses round the table had never seen a black person 'in the flesh'. At the cinema – yes – Gaumont British News illustrating famine or unrest.

Anne thought of pictures in her geography book at primary school, of a tall be-robed man tapping rubber from the bark of a tree in a jungle somewhere; Eileen of the minstrels that appeared some seasons on Blackpool pier; Audrey of slaves on the cotton fields (she had just read *Gone with the Wind*). Margery, considering what this news might mean for the future, thought that there would be black patients one day, here in Merton, and that would mean learning to read a different set of symptoms. Did black skins go pale when sickly or anaemic; flush red in a fever, lips turn blue in heart failure? Not at the moment of any urgent concern.

Then, simultaneously from several mouths came the same question: "What sort of reaction did the patients have?"

"We-ll," said Jane, he kept a bit in the background, you know, but for once all eyes weren't on Dr Anderson!"

Dr Anderson – white, grey haired, immaculate in a dark three piece suit with silver tie, the epitome of the elegant professional gentleman, with a dignity and a voice to match, was the darling of the ward sister (no one of lesser rank was ever allowed near him). He was regarded with awe and respect by the patients, especially the women. He would address them by name, cover a hand with his own and look into their eyes murmuring, "And how

96

are you, Mrs So-and-So?" At this the most grumbling, difficult, hard to please patient would melt, and reply:

"Oh, a lot better, doctor, thank you."

Magic! Known to the staff as 'the Anderson effect' little did the patients know that the great man knew their name because Sister had whispered it to him before leaving the previous bed. And now this paragon of traditional, predictable, behaviour had selected a black man to work within his jurisdiction. Could 'the Anderson effect' accommodate such a change in routine? Time would tell.

A lot was riding on this man's professional skill, his attitude and behaviour. An ambassador for others coming after him and a source of curiosity for those he worked alongside.

The girls finished their mid-morning break, and made their various ways back to the wards to spread the news of this strange phenomenon – a black doctor. Keeping their eyes open along the way, of course, hoping for a glimpse of this exotic individual who had come amongst them.

Night duty was beckoning and then their first outside exam, which if satisfactorily dealt with would earn them each a striped belt. They would expect to complete their first night duty some weeks before this exam so that they were spared the effort of trying to complete one of the three, two hour exam papers after working a ten hour shift on the wards, with whatever that might bring.

Night duty meant moving their rooms yet again to the topmost corridor on the block – thought to be the quietest, away from traffic noise and the clanging lift.

One of the joys of night duty was that again, for most of the time, off-duty was common to everyone. Every morning from 8am until they chose to go to bed there was shopping, the local swimming pool (for some a new found diversion) enjoying a little sunbathing or a game of tennis with one's contemporaries always available. Lectures were a trial as they involved getting up at 6pm, then having three hours to kill before going on duty at 10pm; but more acceptable on the whole than those at 9am, when weariness made concentration difficult.

Most nurses, apart from those who found sleeping during the day almost impossible, enjoyed night duty. There was more true nursing to be done, and less cleaning; Departments – the

e

Laboratory, Physiotherapy, Pharmacy and X-ray all closed their doors, keeping one individual from each department 'on call' in case of emergency need.

If the staff was sparse on day-duty, they were even more so at night. Only three trained nurses were responsible for the whole hospital, as well as being Matron's 'stand-in' for her 'in loco parentis' role in the Nurses' Home.

And what of the ward staffing? Five of the fourteen wards having less than 25 beds boasted only one second year student nurse for the 10 hour shift; with 25 to 35 beds, one first year and one third year nurse, and it was just the Medical Ward and Children's Ward being even larger, that had first, second and a third year student to see to their needs.

The experience gained on night duty was prodigious, the responsibility onerous. But there – the hospital on most nights seemed to settle with a sigh of relief after the hustle and bustle of the day's activities and there was a cosy feeling, almost of intimacy, between the reduced staff numbers. One meal (extra warmed up supper food made principally for the day staff) was served in the dining room in the small hours of the morning – and staff ate it, then sat on to complete their half hour break with a cigarette. . . In the dining room! Of course there were some nights when the work scale increased to 'frantic', but on the whole the tension relaxed, and there was time to really talk to patients, probably at a time when it was most needed.

Night nurses were issued with navy blue woollen capes, with red cross-bands intended to hold them on or off the shoulders – a most glamorous addition to their uniforms and one reminiscent of those worn by the heroines of 'hospital' novelettes. Not often would a utilitarian garment intended for keeping out the chilly draughts of the small hours give a boost to the image, so beloved of romantic authors, of the angel-of-night genre. For lamp read electric torch! Night nurses loved their capes.

It took some time to adjust to porridge, or cereal, toast and the rest at 9.30pm, and even more difficult was meat and two veg, followed, of course, by milk-ur-spunge served at 8.30am.

With most nights less frantically busy than most days, occupation for any quiet periods, more likely to be minutes rather than hours, was catered for by the provision of rolls of gauze. These the night staff were expected to cut into swabs, tie into bundles of six and pack into dressing drums. These were then autoclaved the following day by the porters for use in the theatres. After all, if nurses were not on their feet and on the move, they could still use their hands and improve the shining hour by folding gauze into two inch squares.

Whilst the second and third year nurses folded and packed, the more junior individuals were expected to leave their wards and go to one or both theatres and CLEAN. Probably each of the two operating theatres had been fully functional all the previous day so maintenance had to be carried out at night. All instruments had to be cleaned and placed in sets for sterilising. All the theatre furniture – trolleys, stands, stools and what have you had to be washed in weak carbolic acid and their rubber wheels whitened with liquid ether. And oh! – the rubber gloves. Seemingly endless rubber gloves. Each one had to be inflated to reveal any holes, holes sometimes as tiny as a needle prick, washed in soapy water, dried, turned and dried again then powdered and if time allowed packed into drums for autoclaving. Not a few night nurses dreamt of rubber gloves!

But there, a job shared, like a trouble, is halved, and the nurses didn't dislike their stint in the theatres between 2 and 4am. They sang the popular songs of the day, and not a few rude ones, as they washed and scrubbed, the ward left behind to the tender care of just one nurse. One nurse to thirty beds, and it was quite a disappointment to be recalled to the ward to meet a sudden rise in the pace of need.

If nurses worked long and busy hours, the unfortunate housemen worked even longer ones. The most junior doctors, they came and went for periods of six months at a time, moving on to a different speciality to widen their experience and practice. With no set hours they were 'on call' all day and several nights each week. They did daily ward rounds, they attended pre-admission clinics and the follow up consultations, they assisted in theatre if theirs was a surgical discipline, were the first line of contact for ward sisters or night sisters requiring medical support and the dogsbody for colleagues senior to themselves – 'their consultant and the almost – but-not-quite consultants – the registrars'. In addition, with no permanent medical staff to man the Casualty Department, housemen took it in turns to do this, often working all day and well into the following night. Was it any wonder that pale and weary they took some relief from the sympathetic night nurse, who kept a jug of coffee on the go for them and turned a blind eye if they fell asleep with their heads on the desk, quietly removing the report book from under their mouths if they were inclined to dribble, and substituting a piece of blotting paper!

The responsibility carried by these tired young men was enormous. All agreed that the content of their days and nights as house officers served to concentrate their minds like nothing else. Had the young man with a headache who had, by his own admission been out on the tiles the previous evening, sustained a cerebral haemorrhage or a hang-over? Was this person's appendix ruptured and therefore her pain eased, or had she eaten something disagreeable that was resolving naturally? Decisions had to be made without recourse to a senior man every time such a problem presented. Send such persons home with a couple of Codein or some Milk of Magnesia and risk their return later in danger of demise – a tragedy that had to be lived with. The saving grace of these young men was often the ward sister. With years of experience in one speciality she 'knew her stuff' and many a newly qualified doctor had reason to be grateful to her, or the night sister.

The first time Margery was sent by a night sister to waken a houseman, she went tentatively along the darkened residents' corridors feeling like a player in a bedroom farce. The instructions were – "bang on his door till he answers, then wait till he emerges, otherwise he'll go back to sleep." (Night sisters experience didn't relate exclusively to patients and their troubles.) Eventually, after what seemed like a lengthy two or three minutes, another door opened and a tousled figure clutching his pyjama bottoms appeared and disappeared, presumably to the toilet, muttering that he too had been wakened and was such noise necessary? When the right doctor did put in an appearance Margaret was shocked to find him still in his pyjamas with his white coat tightly buttoned over them, and in bare feet. Silently they made their way back to the ward and the now fully awake doctor did what he had been called to do.

Drinking tea with the night nurses later, his bare feet now propped on a stool, he expressed surprise at his own failure to realise he was barefoot before leaving his room. The pair of woollen operation socks that was found for him completed his bizarre outfit as he slipped and slithered back to bed along polished corridors with instructions to "bring the socks back tomorrow" – ringing in his ears.

It was a matter of wonder to the nursing staff, especially those on night duty, to find how very patient were the patients! Gratitude for the care they were receiving was the overwhelming emotion expressed, and sympathy and appreciation for the volume of work expected of the nursing staff, who they could see scuttling about willing themselves to move faster in their efforts to 'get through'. The level of formal education of the majority of patients was not high; what went on under their skin was a source of mystery to most, who were happy, or more accurately resigned, to leave their treatment to those that knew best. If that treatment was less than successful, if the nursing care less than what they wished, then so be it. Everyone was doing their best. Complaints were very few, recourse to the law even rarer, and when it did occur was the talk of the hospital. After all, this service was free at point of delivery and the age of litigation with its possibility of compensation had not yet arrived. Not infrequently, on enquiring as to the reason why food was being refused, nurses discovered that it was because patients feared to receive a bill they could not meet. Debt was shameful and to be avoided at all costs. "All this lovely food, Nurse, but I've only got my pension so I can't really afford it. . ."

Imagine the amazement and delight, when it was discovered that this wonderful service provided free food as well as medical care. The practice of visitors bringing in food for their hospitalised relatives and friends to enjoy, was one that had established itself over many years and died hard. A basic diet of porridge in the morning, soup at lunch time and tea with bread and jam at 5pm was all that, prior to March 1948, most hospitals provided, so tasty tit-bits were very welcome to enliven this basic regime. Now three meals a day, plus snacks and drinks were provided, but still nurses had to be vigilant in intercepting the offerings sometimes brought in by visitors. A slice of Mum's homemade cake for a young diabetic; a ham sandwich for an individual on a low salt diet – all such items, it had to be advised, were forbidden and should be taken home. All brought on the principle of 'a little of what you fancy does you good' – true sometimes, harmful at others.

New laid fresh eggs brought as a special treat were regarded as something of a nightmare by the night staff. These precious commodities could only be acquired if one knew someone who kept chickens in their back gardens; officially they were 'on ration' and had to have an official stamp on their shells before they were sold. The 'fresh' eggs arrived on the ward and were handed over to whichever nurse was 'on patrol' during the visiting hours; with instructions such as he likes his egg soft boiled for three minutes – or lightly poached on toast – and I've put his name on the shell so he will get his own egg. What an impossibility! Instructions, coming from on high, dictated that patients should not be woken before 6am. In the hour and a half between then and 7.30am when day staff arrived, one nurse may have to see to the bodily needs of around 20 patients. Take and record routine observations; administer four-hourly injections, do a medicine round, complete the night report and serve breakfast. How impossible therefore, to cook perhaps 6 or more eggs in 4 different ways and according to different instructions. In truth patients usually got their own eggs – boiled – for as long as it took for the night nurse to drop what she was doing and dash to the kitchen and take them off the cooker! What a waste, what a failure, what a disappointment. . .

Eileen felt that she was lucky to be allocated to her first night duty during the summer months. They had been enjoying a lengthy spell of unusually fine weather and she found the melting of night into another sunny day quite magical. Too late in the season to hear a true dawn chorus – that joyous greeting of spring produced by dozens of tiny birds, nevertheless it was the birds more mature chirpings and twitterings of parenthood that were the first sign that night was over and another day was arriving. Then the first rays of early sun shot through the monochrome world turning it, bit by bit, into glorious technicolour; rays that grew and grew, making a new day, with its challenges to be met, its opportunities to be discovered. A space in the continuum of time to be filled yet again.

It was the inevitability of it all that got to Eileen, like watching the tide go out as one walked along a beach, and knowing for certain that in a few hours it would come rushing back in again.

Whatever happened during the night, crises, improvement, perhaps death, sleeplessness, pleasure in recovery, anxiety – a maelstrom of emotions, both good and bad, eventually dawn would break and with it would come new hope. All effort paled into insignificance in the face of the enormity, the wonder of creation. Eileen had been brought up to go to Church and Sunday School but it was this wondrous continuation, day by day, of natural events that convinced her, far more than the solemn words of the clergy, that there was an entity, that we call God, 'in charge'. The words she had repeated so often ("hands together, eyes closed children") – "Thy will be done" she felt now that she understood.

With daylight came the early workers. First an individual that Eileen had thought was extinct, the Knocker-Upper. Superseded some years ago by the invention of the alarm clock, here he was, resurrected, considering the need over the war years to manufacture armaments and not items as frivolous and unnecessary as alarm clocks and their components. Who knocked up the Knocker-Upper was unclear. Perhaps he was a chronic insomniac – but here he was making his way along the terraced streets with his long pole on the end of which hung a tassel of metal or ceramic beads, that rattled in a most satisfactory manner against the bedroom windows of his round.

Then came the milkmen, often with horses and carts, the horses needing no instruction as to the route they must take or when and where to stop on their familiar rounds. Small vans delivered bundles of newsprint to be sorted and distributed to the waiting paper boys with their canvas bags, and the first of the mill workers on early shift appeared, some still wearing the traditional Lancashire clogs and shawls, spurned by their younger and more fashion conscious colleagues. Postmen with the first delivery of the day (there were two, sometimes three deliveries a day) and lastly general workers of all kinds and conditions.

All this Eileen glimpsed as she went to and fro, busy with the early morning's work on the ward, registering the outside world through sluice, clinic room or kitchen windows, as a series of snapshots of the awakening outside world.

Sometime between 6am and 8am a bit of that outside world came into the hospital as it had been doing for the last twenty years. Sam.

Twenty or so years ago, Sam a young man in his twenties, married, with a growing family worked for the local council as a dustbin man. Just how it happened was lost in the passage of time but Sam sustained an injury which necessitated the amputation of his right hand. He was in hospital many weeks, but never forgot, with gratitude, the skilled treatment and care he had received during that bleak time. Skill that eventually enabled him to return to work. The cost of an artificial hand was beyond his means, but he learnt to use his good arm and the one that ended in a stump to handle heavy bins. So now Sam came to the hospital every morning before he started work for the council and visited every ward. Here he carried the dirty dressing bins out to the corridor to save the night nurses a job, and from where a porter would collect and empty them later on in the morning. A small task, but much appreciated by the busy night staff. Sam then toured quickly round each bed and picked up any letters that patients needed posting. Twenty years of getting up early, and paying something back to the establishment that had helped him, before he started his work 'proper'. He was known and liked by everyone for his cheerful morning greeting and the perpetual thankfulness that 'his' hospital had done him proud, and now he was able to give something back and would do so for as long as he was needed.

'As long as he was needed.' Ah, there's 'the rub'. For many years local communities had supported their hospital, voluntarily, in many ways, both financially and in kind. They identified with it, were proud of it, and grateful for its presence. It gave focus to charitable effort and, for some, useful justification for rather empty lives. Sam, of course, was a 'one man band' who had found a niche for himself, in something that his limited abilities could offer and did it for the best possible reasons. But for many the 'Lady of the manor' image lingered. She who chaired committees and organised help for the needy carried social status. Committees with rather sentimental titles such as 'The Ladies' Hospital Comforts League' and 'The Association of Hope and Pity' had grown over the years – and now? Were they all to be dissolved as this new National Health Service provided everything everyone could possibly need? Was all the goodwill directed towards their hospital, for whatever reason, to be lost? Was the hospital almoner, now re-named the Medical Social Worker to lose a good chunk of her responsibilities, with no volunteers to organise? The world was shifting – for the good? 'Of course', a thousand times, 'of course', it was for the better but there was always a negative as well as a positive side to change. Not 'our' hospital run by us, locally, for the local people, but a richer more bureaucratic organisation run by faceless people somewhere in London. Ah, well.

One more night! Days were shortening as autumn pushed summer away, and the end of the night duty loomed. It was Sunday morning, and tomorrow – holiday! One year's service – the October '48 intake had taken their first tentative steps into this world of medicine, and now their first full two weeks of holiday was imminent. The original eleven starry eyed hopefuls, that had arrived at Albert Terrace, now reduced to six, still clung to and identified with each other. They had made friends elsewhere, had worked and socialised with many others, but it was here, with their own 'set' that they felt the easiest of fellowship. Jane had nipped home, Margaret gone to morning service at the local Church, and Audrey Renton – well Audrey might be anywhere – she remained largely an outsider. The rest had gathered in Anne's room having a brew and a chat, before going to bed.

It had been quite a busy night. After years of darkness the famous Blackpool Illuminations were back, and with them inevitably came road accidents. It seemed all Lancashire took to the road between Merton and Blackpool, especially on a Saturday evening – hungry for light and glitter. Thousands of light bulbs, carefully stowed away in 1939, were brought out, dusted off, and a semblance of the old yearly spectacles intended to lengthen the season for the many hoteliers and boarding house keepers dependent on the arrival of visitors, were established once again. Every lamp post and building of any note was covered in lights; there were strings of lights – yards and yards of them, in many colours, tableaux depicting fairy tales and Disney characters, and of course, the famous trams that plied the promenade transformed into gondolas, pirate ships, and the like. With very few private cars on the road, every coach firm for miles around ran trips to 'see the lights' with suitable stops en route at pubs and chip shops, of course.

Last night had produced two accidents. Five adults and six children, none of them very badly injured. With a selection of broken bones, cuts, abrasions and bruises and all suffering from shock. Theatre had had to be opened for those needing surgery, and for the rest – frightened, bewildered and crying – their injuries treated and accommodation found, at least over night. Then the day staff could take over, and seek relatives to take them home and arrange to retrieve their abandoned cars. Tomorrow there would possibly be another lot. So far this year there had been no coach crashes. Thank goodness. Such an event would necessitate the 'Major Accident Plan' being put into action. All the student nurses knew of this plan, devised during the war, but had never been made aware of its content. Not a few considered that the personnel involved would probably be as bewildered by it as those it sought to help, if necessity ever demanded its implementation.

Anne, in pyjamas and dressing gown, was stretched out on her bed, the others perched on windowsill or on the bed end. "Two whole weeks to get up when I want to and to eat what I want, when I want – that is when I'm hungry and not when the kitchen staff decree." Anne wriggled in anticipation.

"Two weeks to live something like a normal person who finishes work each day at 5pm, and goes to bed when it's dark," Eileen chipped in.

"Cream, eggs, home cured bacon, roast chicken and vegetables from the garden." Margery was going, with her parents, to stay at a farm in the Lake District, where they had had previous holidays and knew the extent of the farmer's wife's catering abilities. "Bliss."

"No morning panic to 'get through' before the day staff arrive," Jane added, joining them after her quick visit home to check if her 'hard hat' had been delivered. She was going for a week-long riding holiday, a present from her godmother.

"But," wailed Anne, sitting up and clutching her head in mock horror, "two weeks without seeing HIM, how shall I bear it?"

"You're batty," Eileen interjected. "You're far too old to have a crush on anybody, especially a rather nondescript surgeon, who doesn't know you exist. Besides which – he's old!"

For some weeks Anne had been singing the praises of a new registrar who was responsible for the patients on the ward where Anne had spent the last three months as the junior night nurse. He was, according to Anne, wonderful, skilled, handsome, kind, gentlemanly – and sexy!

"He's not old, and besides I like older men, more dependable, wiser more exciting."

"And grey," Eileen added. "Grow up, you'll be decorating the cover of your anat and phys note book with 'I love C.M. – true' next – and what will Miss B-s make of that?"

"He's only grey at the edges," argued Anne. "Distinguished."

"He's not very tall," Margery, who at five foot ten inches herself, judged every man's desirability by his height, added her bit. She considered only men over six feet worthy of attention.

Jane, at the window, was squinting down at the cars parked below. "Old, grey, short or anything else," she squealed, "he's here. Getting into his car!"

There was a concerted rush to the window, and Jane, her eyes dancing with mischief, cried, "Let's send him a love token – from Anne," and seizing Anne's discarded brassiere, tossed it through the window, intending it for the bonnet of the car. Whether her aim was bad or the breeze that morning particularly frisky was uncertain, but the undergarment in question came to rest on a corner of the coping stone that crowned one of the pillars forming the rather grandiose front entrance of the hospital.

Consternation! Weak with laughter they considered what was to be done. To get it down was imperative before anyone saw it and traced it, one size 38" G cup bra, back to its owner. Not a difficult problem.

Meanwhile Doctor Charles Morris, age 38, five foot ten and a half inches tall and with a few grey hairs amongst his curly brown ones, drove placidly home to his wife, children and Sunday lunch. The bra flapped tantalisingly against the brickwork. They tried poking it off with a window pole from the ground but it was too high up. Then someone had a bright idea, if they could get into the room two floors below Anne's room maybe they could fish for it. . .

The individual occupying the correct room was located having her morning break, the problem explained, and she obligingly unlocked her room. The sash window only opened at the top, which proved some difficulty, but they managed to insert Eileen, being the smallest, into the aperture and held tightly onto her legs. The window pole proved inadequate as a fishing rod but she did the next best thing, and sent the itinerant garment fluttering down onto the doorstep below. The speed with which it was retrieved from its resting place defies description! "Thank goodness!" was Anne' reaction. "I only have two bras – and the other one's at the laundry. What would I have worn tonight?"

Chapter Eight

After their very welcome break, the girls returned to work refreshed and with a feeling of tentative curiosity towards what they might meet on the specialist wards – their work stations for the coming year. Gynaecology, Orthopaedics, Genito-Urinary, Ophthalmic, Ear, Nose and Throat, and that mishmash of surgical and medical cases that constituted the private wards.

Hovering over all this conjecture however, like a black impenetrable cloud, was the knowledge that in a very short time their first state exam would be upon them. It blocked out coherent thought of other things, inhibiting enjoyment of free-time, and loomed like a thorny unyielding hedge that they had to get over, or under or through, before they could progress. Lectures increased to two a week, largely consisting of revising those that had taken place long past, and the nurses took to carrying their note books around with them, reading and re-reading them in any spare moment they could find.

As with their PTS exam the girls knew little about what they could expect. The date of the exam, they knew – yes – but the duration? Was it one or two papers on anatomy and physiology? Similarly on nursing practice. . . What was the pass mark? Would there be any choice amongst the questions? Could one sit again if one failed? It seemed that any information, apart from that laid down in the syllabus by the examining body was considered unnecessary, and certainly any attempts to deliver knowledge of exam techniques was lacking in its entirety. Perhaps such ideas were considered suspect by Miss Bailey-Scott, or not within her competency. Margery, and to a lesser extent Jane, attempted to list for the others what they could remember of the golden rules drummed into them at Grammar School. Read all the questions carefully. Be sure you know what is being asked. Answer only what is being asked and don't go off onto a tangent of other things. Allocate time for each question. Perhaps it helped – who knows?

Margery felt reasonably confident of her ability to deal with the anatomy and physiology papers. The "Practice of Nursing" paper was more problematic. The difficulty she found was the discrepancy between what one learnt in the classroom and what was considered acceptable on the wards. The classroom presumed an abundance of equipment, of personnel, and of time – and taught accordingly. In practice, there was a dearth of all these essential ingredients, so on the wards, corners were cut, economies made, improvisation practised. Margery felt that all these manoeuvres were justified because the end result was the same; but would the examiners think similarly? Then there was Evelyn Pierce. Dear old Evelyn had in 1937 written her masterpiece *A General Textbook of Nursing* which most students manage to purchase, and relied on heavily when exams were in the offing. It had been reprinted (and hopefully updated) eight times, most recently in 1945. But how reliable, that is, up-to-date was it? Illustrations showed nurses in ankle length uniforms and in flowing caps, stern faced, wielding fearsome looking implements over recumbent bodies. Evelyn Pierce's casual and very infrequent reference to a 'drug called penicillin' was disturbing, considering its central position in much of today's treatment.

Eileen was the most worried. A good practical nurse, kind, diligent and hard working she would willingly have shown an examiner whatever he wished to know, but writing it down was another matter. Questions such as 'List the functions of the liver', she could cope with, but questions that stated 'Discuss the part played by the spleen in maintaining blood composition', sent her into a minor panic. Whatever, she asked herself, had made her start down this difficult path, when she could be working placidly on a conveyor belt somewhere earning more money with which

110

to save for their future home, waiting for her young man to come home, and with no worries other than planning her wedding day. She knew the answer of course. After twelve months they all knew it. This life, this job, had got under their skins and into their bones. There would be no more departures to fresh fields, they were here to stay the course and beyond. They all felt it – this addiction, this affiliation to the work, but couldn't describe or understand it. The laity called it vocation, the professionals scoffed at the word. Whatever it was that held them they knew that they were hooked. They would continue to grumble about long hours, poor pay, distasteful tasks, difficult patients, and unreasonable superiors, but they would stay, continue to stay, to leave and to return. Meanwhile there was this bloody exam to be dealt with. . .

The exam came, *was* dealt with, and receded after the usual post mortems. They too, receded, and with the careless shrugs which indicated 'Whatever will be will be', life continued.

Audrey Renton was pleased to be allocated to the Gynaecology Ward – back to her origins – this time to a position a little further up the ladder than her erstwhile occupation had earned her. Jane Kirkham went to the Genito-Urinary Ward, known as the Bladder Daddies, and Eileen, with some misgivings to the Private Patients.

It was four weeks before the exam results came through, and it was not with any suggestion of import that Miss Bailey-Scott announced that everyone had been successful. She then gave out individual letters to them all that told them that 'the examiners were satisfied with their performance' and wished them well in their continued training.

Matron arrived, a bunch of striped belts in her hand, and beamed happily at the relieved nurses. She congratulated them and told them that she was proud of their success, a 'stroke' of official admiration and encouragement all the more appreciated for its rarity in a world when failures were more often highlighted, and victories taken for granted. Striped belts were distributed and tried for size. The girls were now recognisable second year students.

How does one celebrate these steps along the way? In fact, they didn't. Month end was still a week away, so no one had any money. Christmas was coming, with all the expense that that entailed. Celebration would have to wait.

When Audrey Renton first stepped onto Alexandra Ward, the Gynaecology Ward, she expected to find a familiar scenario. St Mary's Hospital for women, where she had worked prior to her advent in Merton, had a formidable reputation as a centre of excellence in the North West and Audrey felt that she knew what was what. Things were familiar, in part. The beds were filled with the same sort of patients, with the same sort of needs that she had encountered before, but here the similarity stopped. What St Mary's had lacked and what Merton Royal Infirmary had – was Sister Bennett. Sister Bennett, a legend in the relatively small community of the hospital and in the town of Merton itself, for competency and an efficiency second to none. The story that new and naïve student nurses were told, was that Sister B had learnt her craft as Florence Nightingale's lieutenant at Scutari, or alternatively, as the most junior of juniors who had held the lady's lamp on the famous nightly rounds. Both stories, were, of course, patently untrue, and in fact Sister Bennett was a war widow from the 1914-18 war. After a brief and tragic marriage she had devoted her life to her profession and had served for a number of years in the Queen Alexandra's Royal Army Nursing Service, retiring with the rank of Major. Now back in civilian life, she applied her army experience and standards of discipline to her work in Merton. Consultants respected her; housemen tiptoed nervously round her; and student nurses ran the gauntlet of her tongue. But, my goodness, her patients lacked nothing in their journeys toward recovery. No slackness in any respect was tolerated, the presence of visitors was endured as a necessary evil, and though Sister Bennett could be kind, considerate and sympathetic if she felt a patient warranted such attention, the moaners and those not willing to follow instructions or help themselves as directed, received short shrift.

Into this atmosphere of businesslike efficiency came Audrey Renton who ran and jumped to instruction as many had done before and would do after her. Student nurses (after moving on to another ward) thought that the Sister Bennett experience was a good one which they wouldn't have missed for the world.

If Sister Bennett was careful of her professional attitude and behaviour, the consultant gynaecologist on her ward was the opposite. A rotund bachelor of some fifty years known to the nurses as Grandpa Corby, he certainly was not immune to the presence of the more comely nurses. An arm would linger round a slim waist and a well-rounded bottom might receive a surreptitious pat, whilst sister, if present, pretended ignorance. His attentions were in full view of everyone else and never went any further. He was regarded with tolerant benevolence by those receiving his attentions and it speaks volumes to say that Grandpa Corby always had a string of ex-nurses who asked for his professional care when they returned as young wives to book a bed in the maternity unit. He was a good doctor, and his patients received as an eccentricity his assertions that his seasonal hay fever was 'an allergy to women', nothing more than that!

Audrey, and indeed the rest of the staff on Alexandra were enjoying the fruits of the first upgrading to be undertaken under the new financial regime of the NHS. Completed only a few weeks ago, now green plastic curtains ran on rails round each bed, making screens redundant. One bed at the end of the ward had been forfeited to allow for an area to be partitioned off to form an office and now (oh! happy day) Sister tucked herself into it and abandoned her previous desk. This had always been located in the centre of the ward from where every word spoken, every movement of staff or patient could be noted – enough to inhibit patients conversation and to frighten the uncertain or careless nurses into improving performance PDQ.

The biggest benefit of all, however, was the creation of a day room. The first in the hospital, a large open air balcony at the far end of the ward had been incorporated into the main building and a linen cupboard the size of a small room established, alongside a larger area furnished as a sitting room for those patients that were ambulant. Easy chairs and small tables were in place and, the crowning touch, a pair of blue love-birds chirped companionably in a cage in the corner. The room was well used and popular, not least appreciated by Sister Bennett, who, whilst recognising that patients must be encouraged to get up and walk about when their condition warranted it, hated having patients hanging about and not lying neatly in bed. Now she could herd them into the day room. Much tidier!

It seemed to Audrey, that no matter how many times she went into the day room, the conversation there was always the same. Patients changed, came and went, but the burning question, the topic that consumed all others was – how soon? How soon? How soon on returning home could they expect to resume marital relations? Opinion fell into two camps. Those who couldn't wait to jump into bed with their partners, especially those for whom their hospital stay had resulted in freedom from the fear of unwanted pregnancy. Then there were those who intended to make their incapacity stretch as far as possible and enjoy unbroken nights of sleep! Audrey shrugged, didn't offer an opinion, and left them to it.

The two budgerigars in the day room were providing the staff with unexpected entertainment. They were beginning to talk! First of all very recognisable grunts and ooh's and ah's were forthcoming – just the noises made as the ladies lowered their post-operative bodies into the chairs provided. Audrey thought one of them said 'stitches' but she couldn't be sure. What the nurses were hoping for from the little birds was some repeated bits of the often salacious conversation that went on around them. Nothing doing. . . they were evidently well brought up little birds! Every morning a junior nurse cleaned out the cage, and filled their water and seed pots and every morning by joint arrangement whoever undertook this task repeated the words 'Shucks to Sister Bennett' to the pair. It took three weeks, then one of them uttered the required words – and the second one added, "Eee but my bottom's sore." The nurses hugged themselves in delight.

Of the many patients that passed through Alexandra Ward whilst Audrey was working there, one stood out in her and all the staff's minds for some time. The story emerged bit by bit, with people other than the ward staff making their contributions.

Mick and Angelina arrived in town one day, having travelled over from Southern Ireland on the ferry to Liverpool and then onward to Merton. Why Merton remained a mystery, but arrive they did, with no possessions, no money, and with Angelina heavily pregnant. They found an empty terraced house in a row recently vacated prior to demolition – the council's slum clearance programme was getting underway. They appropriated a few sticks of furniture and an old mattress left behind by the previous tenant, lit a fire with scrap wood, warmed some water, drawn from the public lavatory at the end of the street, and made tea in an old pan.

Mick found work in the nearby wholesale fruit market with 'cash in hand' and no awkward questions asked about addresses, insurance cards and the like. It was the local Health Visitor who found them, guided by the neighbourhood children, whose playground was the street and whose natural curiosity led them to keep track of all the comings and goings around them. They excitedly told her of the 'new' couple living in one of the empty houses. Considering Angelina's condition the Health Visitor called the local midwife and together the two of them visited. Angelina, supported by a stolid and determined Mick, adamantly refused to go into hospital, and as she appeared to be in reasonable health, and her pregnancy normal they reluctantly left promising a return visit. They found, from charitable sources, bedding, baby clothes and a few home comforts and left these on their return, unhappy but resigned with the situation, closing their minds to the legality of the couple's living arrangements.

When the midwife received the message that Angelina was in labour, she drove round immediately, only to find the new mother sitting up and happily suckling a lusty baby boy with red hair – just like his father. The baby was large and the birth had been precipitate, so unfortunately Angelina had torn rather badly and needed stitching. Again hospital was refused so the midwife enlisted the help of a sympathetic GP who did what was necessary by the light of a pocket torch. So far so good.

Things progressed. Mick was bringing in sufficient money for the couple to patronise the local fish and chip shop, Angelina's milk flowed and the baby sucked hungrily.

It was on the fourth day that the midwife arrived to find an agitated Mick, a howling baby and a pale and perspiring Angelina sitting in a pool of blood. Now hospital admission was imperative; she sent for an ambulance, and, anticipating trouble, the police. Angelina now beyond protestation, was lifted into the ambulance, a policewoman took the baby to a 'place of safety' and a fatherly policeman weighing up the little family's circumstances, did little more than advise Mick to 'move on'.

So Angelina arrived at Merton Royal Infirmary. Audrey made up a bed and prepared Angelina for theatre where the cause of her excessive bleeding could be investigated. It seemed, and was later confirmed on enquiry, that Mick had removed his wife's stitches in order to claim his marital rights.

With rest, warmth, food and two pints of someone else's blood, Angelina soon gained colour and strength, but she cried in this strange place. Cried for Mick and for her baby who she had nursed for such a very short time. Looking about 14 years of age, her dark curls tumbling over the pillow, a little more colour in her cheeks and her greeny-blue eyes full of tears, Angelina roused a protective instinct and motherly concern in staff and patients alike. One gave her a pretty nightie, another some scented soap; precious sweet rations were shared with her; but still Angelina wept.

When the time came for Angelina's new stitches to be removed and she was ready for discharge, arrangements were made for her to go to a Mother and Baby Home where hopefully her son would be returned to her.

But first Sister Bennett resolved she must talk to Mick and make him understand that their lifestyle (including his treatment of his wife) was not acceptable. The nurses, anticipating her intentions, did their best to eavesdrop when Mick was invited into the office. Ten minutes later he emerged – not abashed, ashamed or even angry at the sister's interference but embarrassed and confused. Embarrassed that this strange woman should talk to him – a man – about such intimate things. How shameless of her, how hard-faced, now lacking in decent behaviour! And this condemning of his actions! Didn't she understand that they were *married*? Married, in the sight of man and of God, so of course he could expect his rights. England was a strange place indeed.

Nonplussed, sister decided she must talk to Angelina about contraception. She took a cervical cap and a packet of condoms to her bedside and gently explained their use. Angelina was horrified. "Dere wicked, dem tings, wicked," she sobbed. Between gasps she explained, "My Mick is a turrible good cat-o-lic. . ." and repeating the word 'wicked' she turned over and pulled the sheet over her head. Sister Bennett retired – beaten. She had tried.

Mick visited his wife and son in The Home each evening, and each evening they pushed their baby, in a borrowed pram, round the nearby park.

On the fourth day they never returned from their evening stroll. The pram was found later at the railway station. The little family were off to find another place, another town, and there probably they would make more little red-haired babies.

Human flotsam, which in spite of compulsory education, a

welfare state and well meaning charities, is always with us. But then, inside every baby born there is potential – not always fulfilled – but there all the same.

Around 2000 years ago, a long way from Merton, wasn't a baby born to another itinerant teenage girl? Born in a stable?

There was no doubt about it, everyone agreed that Maurice Ward smelt. A men's Genito-Urinary Ward popularly known as the Bladder Daddies, it didn't have the disgusting smell of stale urine so often found in geriatric wards and old people's homes – but a smell of something not unpleasant and certainly more distinctive. That Maurice Ward *didn't* smell of urine was a credit to the staff who emptied, changed, mopped, scrubbed and generally laboured mightily in their endeavours to comfortably accommodate twenty or so patients virtually all of whom had unreliable bladders. The Maurice Ward smell clung to the nurses' dresses and they carried it with them as a sort of badge that advertised their workplace, the aroma getting stronger as the week progressed, for with only two dresses, one on their backs and one in the laundry, there was no alternative but to wearing a smelly dress. Perhaps the smell came from its age and the building materials used for the ward construction, overlaid with carbolic, Dettol and liquid ether (widely used as a skin cleanser) that pervaded both there and the rest of the hospital. Who knows? Certainly the building left a lot to be desired. It was generally understood that Maurice Ward had been erected to accommodate war wounded, but the wounded from *which* war was open to question. Built as an annexe and connected to the main hospital by an enclosed corridor, it was a wooden construction that resembled, from the outside, an elongated cricket pavilion. When it rained hard, and the wind blew in a certain direction, the roof leaked and nurses had to arrange receptacles to catch the drips. Though connected to the central heating system, the radiators never got very hot and that, plus the lack of insulation in the walls, meant that the ward was chilly. Night nurses shivered in their woollen capes, and the patients wore thick jumpers in bed brought in by their concerned relatives, and were also known to sit up for meals with blankets draped round their shoulders.

Although the ward catered for men needing surgery to kidneys, bladder and all the bits and bobs and ins and outs of the parts between, by far the majority of patients came to Maurice Ward because of their enlarged prostate glands, there to have the offending organ removed. Because an enlarged prostate is an affliction of older men it was only seldom that Maurice Ward accommodated anyone under the age of fifty years – old leaky men in an old leaky building!

This was the prospect that greeted Jane as she arrived to start her three month stint among the Bladder Daddies. But Maurice Ward was, as she and others before her had found, a happy ward. It had windows that looked out onto lawns and trees; one of the few wards in the hospital that had accessible views of the outside world – and it had Sister Fortune.

Physical surroundings for someone not well, uncertain, perhaps frightened and worried are important but come second in value to the quality of the people that are there to see to their needs and treatments; to talk to them, understand and inform them. All sick people need staff that are relaxed, have confidence in their own abilities and can communicate confidence and belief in recovery to their patients.

How do the Jane Kirkham's of this world acquire such valuable skills? Well, in part it is within themselves, in part learnt in the training school, but in the main it permeates from more senior staff. Sister Fortune ran Maurice Ward with relaxed efficiency. . . "Yes, a beloved grandchild could visit, providing he or she behaved," – child visitors were usually barred – "Yes – Dad could smoke his smelly old pipe – but not at meal times." Yes, she'd find a radio, in time for the patients to hear the local match broadcast, and so on. She gave staff an extra half hour 'off duty' on a Sunday provided the work was accomplished satisfactorily. She let them enjoy left over ice cream behind the kitchen door and didn't object if they ate sweets (always available from patients) whilst doing boring cleaning jobs. She gave praise when it was earned, and thanked individuals for special effort; she chided and instructed, got cross at times, but looked always for improvement. And, of course, the atmosphere rubbed off onto the staff, influenced their attitudes and behaviour and made a happy ward. To the patients, Sister Fortune was sometimes the 'busy daughter doing her best for her old dad' sometimes a valued confidante. When she thought it would help, she flirted gently,

118

but whatever ploy she practised she usually got her own way with even the most recalcitrant old buffer. When patients left, their opinion was generally that she was 'a grand lass', who knew her stuff – and you can't get a better testimonial than that.

What strange and varied reasons lead us into our chosen professions. Anne Fortune's parents both teachers had expected their daughter to follow in their footsteps, but she had other ideas. Her name was the difficulty. The prospect of having successive hoards of children calling her Miss Fortune was not to be contemplated – she would acquire another title and become Nurse Fortune and later Sister Fortune and NOT spend her life as a misfortune. Teaching's loss was nursing's gain.

Maurice Ward was temporarily without a staff nurse, the last one having left to further her career by starting midwifery training. This made life difficult for the one trained nurse on the ward's staff establishment, so Sister Fortune could only take her 'off duty' if she remained 'on call' in the building – or found a colleague to take her place. It was therefore with some relief that it was announced that a new staff nurse had been appointed and would start work at the beginning of next month. This was news indeed, as it was seldom that staff from 'outside' were employed. Both staff nurses and sisters were practically all 'home grown' trainees that qualified, possibly left to take further study and then returned to permanent positions. When Maurice Ward's complement of student nurses came on duty at 7.30am on the first of December, they were surprised to find a man sitting at the desk reading the night report. Jaws dropped as they realised that this particular man was wearing a short white jacket, with navy blue epaulettes and an SRN badge. A male nurse, a man, the new staff nurse was. . . CRIKEY! a man! He turned with a grin. "Hello, I'm Staff Nurse Carruthers – I came in a bit early as I've got twenty-five patients to 'learn' – all new to me, and I'll be looking for some help from you lot!"

Here was a turn up for the book. They'd heard of male nurses, of course, in mental hospitals – but not in *proper* hospitals – like theirs! Walking over to the main building at 9.30am for her lunch, Jane pondered. If this chap was an SRN which he was, then he must have proved himself competent to nurse women and children, and he could possibly be asked to work on such as Alexandra Ward. Her mind baulked at such an idea. But why not?

They nursed men didn't they as a matter of common practice? So!? She chortled to herself, and couldn't wait to tell the others – first a black doctor and now a male nurse. Jane Kirkham, town crier, was back in business.

Over the day more facts emerged. Staff Nurse Carruthers had been in the regular army, had done his training there, and had seen service with the RAMC in some pretty hairy places. He was married, had a child, and most amazing of all, lived out of the hospital in a council house on a neighbouring estate – just as if he had a proper job!

Here was a hot new topic on which tongues and imaginations could get busy. "It's not natural," this from a third year nurse, busy knitting something grey and shapeless, as she sat, shoes off, in the nurses' lounge that evening. "Nursing is woman's work. We have the caring, nurturing genes that go with wombs and hormones to make us suitable. What man wants to do women's work?"

"Perhaps he's – you know – queer! Ladies' hairdressers and male nurses are all definitely suspect." Audrey Renton was putting in her two-pennyworth of knowledge.

"How can you tell?"

"Dunno."

"You can't tell – but this chap is bald, is about 40, wears glasses and has a wife and family." Jane found herself defending the new staff nurse, but she didn't know quite against what. Malicious gossip perhaps.

"I don't know what wearing glasses has to do with sexuality, but I do know that all homosexuals aren't like the Billy Mints of this world you know." Margery Harvey in reality knew less than nothing about the subject, decent people just didn't consider such things; let alone talk about them; but all the nurses knew about Billy Mint – a hospital regular.

Billy Mint appeared often in the Casualty Department and sometimes on the wards; a young man prone to hanging around street corners in the town centre. He had aggressively dyed red hair and wore lipstick and eye shadow, facts that were not to be tolerated by the young bloods of the town. Saturday nights saw him usually escorted by a policeman arriving with black eye, burst lip or worse, for another stitch in time.

Why Billy Mint was still free to behave as he did was a

120

mystery. Homosexuality was a crime that carried a prison sentence, but then – would Billy have lasted long in prison? The sexuality of Staff Nurse Carruthers soon ceased to be a subject of speculation. He worked hard and could 'get through' with the best and that was what mattered. If he got promoted to Sister, Anne Manning pondered, would one address him as Brother? And if, her fertile and imaginative brain was working overtime, if he ever became a matron? What then? The phrase 'Matron's had me on the mat' could have a whole new meaning. . . Ha ha!

f

Chapter Nine

One, two, three. . . eight. That should be enough. Jane carefully counted spoonfuls of tea into the large pot and put it on to the draining board to brew whilst she mustered cups and saucers onto the top of the ward's tea trolley.

Every bed on Maurice Ward had a visitor by its side, so with a bit of encouragement, they, the visitors, might be persuaded to give generously for a cup of tea before making their way home. This was part of the grand plan to raise enough money to purchase decorations for the ward this coming Christmas, and if possible buy each patient, unlucky enough to be resident at that time, a small present. So far they were doing well. The nurses had worked out that if every pot of tea brewed during the week was made just slightly less strong, then enough of the ward's tea ration might be gathered to provide an extra pot on the two visiting days. Sell the tea to the visitors and, 'Bob's your uncle', a jingling jangling nest egg with which to purchase some Christmas cheer.

Jane splashed a little tea into the sink so that she might assess its colour, and satisfied, set off with her loaded trolley. Friendly rivalry existed between the wards as to which could contrive the best Christmas transformation, and they were all intent on finding enough money to do just that. Some wards ran raffles with goods begged from local shops as prizes, while others blatantly begged, with a bucket placed at the ward door bearing a sign stating 'For patients' comforts this Christmas'.

Decorations would go up on Christmas Eve and come down on the morning of the 27th – a two day hiatus in the life of the hospital, when rules relaxed and patients, as far as was safely possible, were discharged home, their beds left empty. Emergency admissions only were accepted, until normal working was resumed on the 27th. Departments and clinics were closed, except for one individual 'on call' for each discipline and NONE of the nursing staff was allowed holiday, a day off, or indeed any off-duty whatsoever on December 25th. So – fewer patients and maximum staff presence.

The previous Christmas of course, the girls had been on holiday at the end of their PTS and not then on the ward establishment, so the coming season was the first they had experienced in residence. Tales abounded. Sister on Jenner Ward always got legless entertaining consultants with sherry before their customary carving of the ward's turkey. Grandpa Corby invariably took Sister Bennett, for once flustered, into a clinch before demonstrating his skill with a carving knife, and the larger of the two operating theatres was open for dancing to the strains of a borrowed gramophone brought in especially for the occasion. Paper hats could be worn instead of caps and patients were allowed as many visitors as could be accommodated, including children.

Casualty, of course, remained open – and busy. The population of Merton popped their appendices and stomach ulcers, strangulated their hernias and walked under buses, despite the day. In addition children fell off their new bikes within hours of Father Christmas making his deliveries. Small children swallowed the novelties found in crackers, and bigger children the lucky silver sixpences it was the custom to hide in Christmas puddings – not so lucky!

The prize however, for the most bizarre accident of 1949, went to two young dads, who, seeking to amuse their respective offspring, had each stuck one of the new bath-time toys now available in the shops, onto their own foreheads. These brightly coloured creations were meant to be fixed to the inside of the child's bath by means of a strong rubber sucker, but once the "Look at Daddy, he's a spaceman," joke had run its course they found they couldn't get the things off! Eventually they left, each with a perfect circular, and no doubt painful, bruise in the centre

123

of their foreheads, and the laughter of the staff concerned ringing in their pink and embarrassed ears.

Eileen had started her Private Patients ward experience with mixed feelings. Her knowledge of patients who chose to pay for what they believed would be an improved service was limited to shots taken on newsreel cameras for the cinema screen. Shots of perhaps royalty leaving such places as the London Clinic, Matron in attendance and a limousine at the door. She had no experience either of what she called 'posh people'. People who paid large sums of money not to have the indignity of lying in a public ward, must be, in Eileen's estimation, posh indeed – or famous – and a town like Merton was unlikely to produce many of the latter. Would private patients treat her like a lady's maid? Expect and demand immediate relief from any twinge of discomfort? Look down from the elevated status that money had bought them and complain vociferously about anything and everything?

In effect, none of these misconceptions proved to be true. Private patients, in spite of the large sums of money their hospital stay was costing them, behaved in the main exactly like patients on a public ward, expressing gratitude for services rendered, showing fortitude in the face of pain and discomfort and confiding the fears and anxieties common to all those facing surgery or a dreaded diagnosis, whatever the length of their purse. Of course, there were those who rang their bell for attention with tiresome frequency, but then public wards produced some of those too, who, in the absence of bells, roared for attention!

Just how much money PPs parted with in order to experience the commercialism that the consultants had fought so hard to retain, was unknown to the student nurses. Perhaps Sister knew, – she certainly spent a lot of time listing the drugs, laboratory investigations, and X-rays that her patients received and for which they would get a bill. Then there were the consultants' fees and those of the anaesthetist, if one was required.

Some years before, when the notion of a free health service was beginning to have substance, consultants, aware of their vital role in any sort of future service, had dug in their heels and said an unequivocal "No!" Aneurin Bevin, the Minister of Health's reply to this threat of non-participation had gone down in history: "I will fill their mouths with gold," was the quote, and the result was that private wards and public wards in NHS hospitals could run alongside each other. Consultants could draw a salary from the State and could also have private patients in the same or a separate establishment.

In truth the Private Wards made an income also for the hospital. They too added their account for the 'board and lodging' aspect of the patient's stay. And the nursing? That was thrown in with the room and bed and any resulting monies went of course to the management.

Eileen enjoyed her time with PPs. With only ten patients when at capacity, there was more time to get to know them as individuals and not just as the recipients of prescribed treatments as delivered by you, their carer. Their stay was longer. If a few more days recuperation was needed – then so be it – patient turnover of less importance. The nearest Eileen ever got to the reflected glory of nursing a famous person was a sad disappointment. The local MP had a mild heart attack whilst attending a political rally in the town, and arrived one day escorted by a flurry of Labour League of Youth members in support. On another day a member of the local football team was admitted to have an incipient in-growing toenail attended to. How unglamorous! The MP, elected in 1947 for the first time, had his eye on his ratings for the next general election and was anxious not to project a 'sick man' image, so discharged himself the following day. The footballer's only fan appeared to be the paper boy who toured the wards each afternoon selling the *Lancashire Evening Post*. He worked up a nice little side line begging autographs and then selling them at 2d a time to his mates.

Two patients stood out in Eileen's memory of her time on Private Patients. A couple in their early fifties, both of whom had been widowed some years ago, and each with adult children. They had found each other through their associated occupations and had become engaged to be married. He with a hernia that needed repair and she more seriously with a bowel complaint, they had opted to have their operations at the same time on the same ward. That they should occupy a double room (there were 4 double and 2 single rooms) stretched the principles of propriety and respectability just too far, so they had rooms next to each other and could converse only at the tops of their voices. Togetherness in exceptional circumstances! The day would begin with a bellowed, "Good morning, darling," and continue from there until sheer exhaustion drove them to silence. Then the families would arrive and grandchildren scuttered between the two rooms. Theirs was a far from private courtship. He stayed in hospital for some days after his scheduled date for discharge, until his fiancée was also ready to return home. Then the families arrived and there was a double departure, the good wishes of the staff following them down the corridor. Being involved in the lives of such people, Eileen thought, was much more fulfilling than dancing attendance on some minor film star. . . Wasn't it?

After several weeks on Private Patients, Eileen considered as many had done before her, just how difficult it was for staff to give a good service, and how few were the advantages for the patients who were paying dearly for the privilege of private medicine.

The patients' rooms and the necessary rooms that serviced them had been contrived from what had been the side-wards of the two adjacent surgical wards on the ground and first floors. Between the floors was a steep and rather narrow flight of stairs and an ancient and cumbersome lift. The kitchen was on the ground floor, as was the bathroom, the clinic room on the first floor and each floor, thankfully, had a small sluice room. If the one nurse on duty – staffing levels were commensurate with the number of beds – was attending a patient on the first floor she couldn't hear patients' call bells on the ground floor, and vice-versa. Food had to be carried upstairs from the kitchen and arrived at the bedside cold. Patients upstairs had to be transported downstairs for a bath – and the lift wasn't always available. Meanwhile nurses were up and down, up and down stairs countless times a day.

The rooms were tiny, just large enough to hold a standard bed and locker and one upright chair. The walls were covered from floor to ceiling in shiny green tiles and one small high window was the only ventilation. In these cell-like rooms patients were served the same food, on the same thick crockery provided for all, with no choice for, or pandering to, fickle appetites.

As far as Eileen could see there was only one advantage to paying a consultant for his exclusive services. A patient could choose the day on which he would be admitted – there was no question of going on a waiting list – and his or her surgery was performed by the man himself, no matter how minor the undertaking, and it would be scheduled early in the day. There the advantages stopped as the patients' 'after care' undertaken on public wards by a consultant's registrar and houseman was not available to the private patient, and so not infrequently their place was taken by the ward sister receiving instruction from an absentee consultant over the phone.

Ironically the 'great advantage' anticipated by a PP – that of having visitors, including children, at any time, proved a damp squib. The single rooms were too small to squash them in and sitting on the corridor waiting your turn soon lost its appeal.

So would the current practice of selling dearly a service inferior in many ways to that received free of charge by the rest of the population survive? It would seem so. There was no shortage of people willing to pay to occupy the claustrophobic isolation cells, and to ring their bells fruitlessly for a nurse, willing, but out of earshot. All to avoid what was seen as the indignity of lying in a public ward. But then the consultant was ever so friendly, came to see them three times in one week and always remembered their name. To some that's worth a lot.

Life went on. Lectures had moved on too, and were now given by consultants expounding on their particular speciality. Dr Anderson, he of the exemplary bedside manner, the polished accent and the immaculate presence, proved also to be an excellent lecturer as well as a competent physician. For years afterwards Margery could recall his lectures (and her accompanying notes) on the haemolytic diseases of the new born. Erythroblastosis Fetalis was such a very satisfying term. Sufficiently multi-syllabled and obscure to arouse respect and awe in the uninitiated – but well, not easy to work into everyday conversation! With increased knowledge and the mind-focusing experience of another night duty – this time, for many, as the nurse in charge, confidence grew. Grew, until time after time, a new case, a situation not yet experienced, or an unexpected outcome would jolt an individual out of complacency and into yet another challenge. Lectures, when on night duty, were often a real burden, but necessary if one was ever to understand the vagaries, the endless intricacies of the human mind and body. On one occasion an incident at one of these wearisome morning classroom sessions occurred that was to mark the start of possible changes to a student nurse's future training.

General surgery, and the consultant giving the lecture was in full flow on the gastro-intestinal aberrations that occupied so much of his mind and his time, and with which he was attempting to educate the nurses. It had been a particularly hectic night and all the class after ten hours of intense mental and physical effort had had a substantial meal, were warm, sitting down, and fighting the sleep that their bodies craved. Suddenly their was a crash and Jane Kirkham fell out of her chair into the passageway between the desks. She had lost the battle to stay awake, had slumped sideways and fallen. Of course, the jolt woke her and she climbed wearily back into her chair, gave up the fight and flopped forward, her head on her notes – and snored. There was a horrified silence. Miss Bailey-Scott in her customary desk alongside the lecturer's podium was thunder-struck, but it was the surgeon who took matters into his own hands. Addressing the tutor, and not the class, he looked quickly at the tired listless faces and the slumped bodies in front of him and said, "This is ridiculous. These girls are exhausted. They can't possibly be expected to learn anything. You are wasting their time – and mine." With that he marched out followed by a pink and furious Miss Bailey-Scott.

It was understood that a letter went from the surgeon to Matron and to the Chairman of the Hospital Management Committee, regarding what he considered to be 'the impossible conditions imposed on student nurses whose classroom training was delivered in their own free time and in addition to and after working very lengthy hours.'

It would be nice to say that the lives of student nurses were immediately transformed, but of course no consultant, no matter how enraged he was at the waste of his precious time, could make that happen. But several of the leading nurse training schools were now introducing what was known as the block system, whereby two months of every year were spent in school, nine months on the wards and of course one month on holiday – a massive change and one that it was thought should be considered, separating formal training from the practical experience of ward work.

It would take some time, of course, but these were innovative

128

days and even some of the old school diehards like the Scaly-Bott and the older sisters had eventually to concede that things needed to change. Other opportunities, other careers were opening up for intelligent girls and if nursing was to develop into a profession in its fullest sense and attract sufficient young women to accept the life it offered, then the training had to alter to comply with modern standards and conditions.

"Perhaps even," said Jane Kirkham portentously, "the time may come when wards have a permanent staff of trained nurses and sort of 'nursing aids' to do routine stuff. Then student nurses could spend their time being just that, in its fullest sense – learning, observing and *doing* only under strict supervision."

"Pie-in-the-sky."

"Off your rocker."

"In your dreams."

No one could imagine such a wonderful system.

"In the meantime," said Eileen. "Jam yourself tightly into your desk, and choose one next to the wall, so that if you must fall asleep you won't litter the aisle."

It really was most annoying. Back on day duty and Margaret Wood remembered, an hour or so into the day's work, that she had forgotten to put her laundry – soiled uniform and bedding – outside her bedroom door for the laundry man to collect. That would mean making one dress, one set of collar and cuffs and seven aprons last for a fortnight – an unthinkable option. The alternative was spending her mid-morning break carrying the bag across to the laundry, apologising for her earlier omission, and hoping that it wasn't too late to add her contribution to the pile of nurses' laundry awaiting attention.

She'd never had cause to visit the laundry or even consider its existence as a part of the hospital's industry. Clean laundry arrived every Tuesday morning, was replaced with soiled articles and put out for collection on Wednesdays. With no washing facilities, beyond the hand basin in their bedrooms, available to the nurses, and nowhere to dry washing, do-it-yourself was out of the question, except for small personal items. So the laundry it had to be, providing you remembered to fit in with its schedule.

Pushing open the door of the laundry, the damp heat hit her.

Margaret spied some commercial sized washers churning away on the far wall, but there were also vast sinks, vats and sort of cauldrons, steaming with hot soapy water containing or awaiting more articles of washing. Steam hung everywhere and condensed on things and on persons, the floor wet, and everywhere dripping. Tending this hive of industry, were a number of young women wearing wooden soled sandals and wrap-around overalls, and Margery suspected little else. Many had their hair tightly wrapped in curling pins, the rest their hair a mass of frizz above glistening faces.

Spying a heap of familiar laundry bags lying where they had been dumped, Margery added hers to the pile and looked around for someone to whom she could apologise for her lateness. She hadn't long to wait. A stout, red-faced woman, a name badge proclaiming 'LAUNDRESS' pinned to her ample bosom, was approaching.

"And exactly what do you think you're doing, young woman?" The voice was aggressive, challenging, hostile.

Margaret apologised, explained her lapse.

"The trouble with you bloody nurses is you never think of anybody but yourselves. You get your washing done, your meals made, and your rooms cleaned, but you can't take the trouble to put out your bags on a Wednesday. You make me sick."

The laundress was working herself into full flow, the audience of laundry workers thoroughly enjoying the spectacle of someone other than themselves feeling the lash of the laundress's tongue.

Margaret couldn't believe her ears. She'd said she was sorry and brought the bag down herself, surely this tirade was unnecessary? It was when the laundress followed up with: "You're idle, idle, too bloody idle to pull the chain on your own shit," – that Margaret felt that this woman had gone too far and turning on her heel walked away, the laundress's voice yelling, "Come back here you little toe-rag – I haven't finished with you yet!" following her. Margaret kept on walking. Phew! What a dreadful course, vulgar woman, she thought. Those poor girls. Imagine working in that sort of atmosphere and for someone like that. Ward sisters might be authoritarian, demanding and sometimes unfair – but they remained ladies.

Soon, engrossed in the busy life of the ward, Margaret forgot the incident until that evening at supper time as she received her baked beans and chips from the home sister, the sister said, "Ah Nurse Woods, I understand you were rude to the laundress this morning."

Margaret was dumbstruck. That dreadful woman had taken the trouble to report her – in the hope presumably that she would receive an official reprimand. Margaret couldn't remember saying anything other than apologising. Had she been rude? Then it dawned on her. "I turned my back on her and walked away," she told the sister, then repeated just what had been said. "I don't believe I need to listen to that sort of invective," she concluded.

The home sister nodded. "No Nurse, you do not," she said. "Just remember to put your laundry out in future!"

Good news, good news, goods news. This wonderful generous, amazing National Health Service was going to make Sam an artificial hand – for free! He told everyone and couldn't wipe the smile off his face in the telling of it. He'd only been to the doctor to pick up the prescription for his wife's codein, (she'd suffered for years with chronic arthritis) and the doctor had suggested he refer him, Sam, to the prosthesis centre in Manchester. Sam had a little difficulty getting his tongue round this strange word, but had been most impressed by what he saw there. They didn't just make the new arms and legs, they also taught you to use them too. The future for Sam was exciting. In another few weeks, after 20 odd years, he was going to be whole again and he couldn't wait to show off his new hand to his friends at the hospital.

When the new hand was finally fitted it took some time to get used to having an arm that was suddenly longer than before. It kept getting in the way and knocking things over, but Sam persisted and loved demonstrating how he could pick up small objects with his new fingers. "Sprung, they are you see," he explained. "There's a chap at the centre can handle a cigarette. Get it in and out of the packet and everything."

Well done the rehabilitation staff. What a useful accomplishment!

Good news, bad news. The good news of Sam's new arm had flashed round the nurses' dining and sitting rooms with pleasure in its telling. The bad news, or more accurately sad news, that followed it, crept with funereal snail-like pace that brought a

131

mixture of emotions in its wake. Barbara Bouncey was dead. The little girl who had been a patient at the hospital for endless months, longer than many of the staff had been in employment there, had died during the previous night. All but a few of the nursing staff had at some time had involvement in the endless battle to give the child some sort of quality of life; all had felt a great sympathy and compassion for her, alongside a quickly suppressed desire to smack her bottom. Of course it was accepted that the child's bodily suffering and her knowledge, imperfectly understood, that she was the cause of the rancour that divided her parents, had turned her from a sunny carefree toddler, into the spiteful selfish, manipulative child that had 'ruled' over the Children's Ward, earning her the dislike and hostility of the other child patients and the exasperation of her nurses.

After endless surgery to repair or remove parts of her injured body, the complex drug regime that sought to bolster or replicate her impaired functions, and the secondary drug doses that were necessary to reverse the unwanted effects of the first – what had actually proved fatal? Measles. Measles – that childhood illness regarded by many parents as an unremarkable 'Right of Passage', unavoidable and unpleasant but soon over and done with. Sadly, for some, especially for those with underlying conditions measles could kill, and many children died each year as winter epidemics raged; from the disease itself, or its complications.

Of course, children were not knowingly admitted to the ward suffering from infectious diseases. For those needing hospital care there was an isolation hospital – the erstwhile fever hospital – at the other side of town. Unfortunately though, children were admitted for a variety of reasons to the General Children's Ward who were also, unknowingly, incubating something nasty and were already infectious. By the time the symptoms were manifest the damage was done and others were infected and the ward had to close to further admissions. Barbara Bouncey was the latest victim.

It was not usual for hospital staff to attend the funerals of their patients, but in Barbara's case an exception was made and Sister and six or so nurses joined family and neighbours in Church for the interment service. Margaret Woods was one of those attending, hoping that the service might achieve some sort of closure for herself and indeed for everyone. United in their common grief, could there be a mellowing, a softening of the violent antipathy that Barbara's parents and the extended families, felt for each other? Seeing them meet and greet, Margaret thought perhaps there was. Here was something to hope for.

As the funeral party moved to the graveside, the group from the hospital, feeling that these most poignant moments should be for the family alone, left and made their several ways back to the hospital and their on-going commitments.

A few days later, Children's Ward Sister was sitting in her office, deep in her weekly chore of requisitioning the replacement supplies, the everyday bits and pieces that her ward needed, when a young man arrived, unannounced and unexpected. He was angry. Sister recognised him vaguely as one of the many relatives who had visited during the months of Barbara Bouncey's sojourn on the ward and as one of the mourners at her funeral.

"I", the young man announced, "am Barbara Bouncey's uncle, and I have come to tell you that we are not satisfied, and we're making an official complaint about your management of this ward. *You* killed her. She was under your care and she caught measles and died. *Your* fault – and how you had the nerve to come to the funeral and sneak off early, I don't know," he added. "You haven't heard the last of us – I can tell you that for free – and we'll see what the *Evening Post* thinks about it too. OK?" At which the young man stormed out.

The open door, the raised voices, the unusual altercation had drawn many staff to the office, and what had passed there soon became general knowledge. Shaken by the vehemence, worried by the accusations, Sister went to talk to Matron.

"For the time being," said that lady, "we do nothing. We wait and see. You must not let this family worry you unduly. I don't need to tell you that 'fault' doesn't enter into the situation. If an official complaint is made then we will have a properly conducted enquiry into the whole affair – and hope that something positive comes out of it." She sighed. "Attention seeking and scandal mongering via the local press is another matter. That could, quite unjustly, damage the trust parents have in our efficiency and ability to care for their children, and is to be avoided if possible. But we can't do a thing about it without involving others and breaking confidentiality. We are blessed with a free press, and newspaper proprietors need to sell their papers." And Matron repeated her advice "Let's wait and see."

Of course, Sister and her staff worried. Such accusations were rare, threats of publicity even rarer, and though everyone accepted that no true blame was warranted, no one wanted to see their name splashed across a news sheet. Not a few thought guiltily of the times they had felt, after a particularly difficult exhibition of bad behaviour on Barbara's part, 'I could murder that child'. 'So', Margaret Woods thought, 'I was right'. The two feuding and fighting families had become reconciled, but for the worst of reasons – that of presenting a united front in their condemnation of the hospital and its staff.

She felt miserable, tired of the whole situation, overwhelmed by the iniquities of life and of people, and wanted most desperately to feel Roger's arms around her and to talk to him, to just be with him and there to find calm and some understanding.

Margaret's faith was strong. She believed with unwavering certainty that Barbara had found peace, and sanctuary and was now in the arms of the Lord. It was what happened here on earth that worried her, that threw up such unanswerable questions. She wanted to scream WHY? WHY? WHY? at the sky, at the streets, the houses of this dirty little town, and the whole unsatisfactory world. Of course she didn't scream. She went to the place where she had always found comfort, to Church. There she sat in the front pew, quite alone and opened her mind to an incoherent wordless prayer for understanding.

After a while she became aware of someone kneeling alongside her. The vicar, who was also the hospital chaplain, had seen her tear-stained face and was offering his silent, sympathetic presence. In the unexpected relief of not being alone, Margaret pushed her Christian beliefs, her professional persona and her identity as an independent capable young woman on one side and wailed, "I want Roger, I need him."

The vicar squeezed her hand. "I know," he said, "but I'm afraid you are stuck with just me. I'll make a cup of tea. . ."

Sitting in the vestry, Margaret spoke of her disillusion with people, and her anger with God for allowing Barbara's suffering and the malice that He'd let fester in her family; malice that was now turned unfairly on those who had done their best to help her. She ended miserably with: "Why bother? To create a being 'in

134

His image', and then destroy it, slowly and painfully creating discord and unhappiness along the way. What was the point? What purpose had been served? None."

"Not true," the vicar was decisive. Think of the caring and compassion, and the desire to help that Barbara engendered in others. The patience needed, the battles against the negative feelings, battles that the nurses won in spite of their natural inclination. Can anyone or anything that promotes such emotions be useless? Think of the knowledge gained from her condition and her behaviour that can be used to help other patients in the future."

"Mm. . ." Margaret only half believed him. "Such meagre gains – for the price – and what about her family's behaviour?"

"Complaints," came the answer, "no matter how unjustified, help us to look hard at our actions and perhaps find better different ways of doing things. Neither you nor I, nor your Roger, can fully understand, we must just trust that His ultimate purpose is for good. I won't insult you with a parsonical quoting of 'God moves in a mysterious way', but by golly – He sure does!"

Matron's importuning of a 'wait and see' policy proved to be a wise one. The Bouncey family did complain and the management committee investigated the complaint, concluding that it was unjustified and expressed satisfaction at the way the ward was run. They added that in the absence of a quick and efficient test to detect infectious diseases before admission or soon afterwards, and with only a limited number of specific vaccines available, nothing more could have been done. They sent a letter to the family expressing their sympathy and that of the many staff who had cared for Barbara during her long illness and expressed the belief that they had found no neglect in her case.

The *Lancashire Evening Post* decided that the factual reporting of the events that led up to Barbara Bouncey's illness and death would serve no useful purpose and may even do harm. In effect they refused to feature the dead girl as a martyr to bureaucratic neglect. Well done, the often criticised popular press.

Chapter Ten

"Inky Pinky Ponky, my daddy bought a donkey." Margery was carefully easing the dressing off a five-year-old's operation wound, and had, from experience found that reciting nonsense rhymes sometimes helped – making potentially unpleasant procedures that bit more tolerable.

Richard had been admitted to Children's Ward some ten days earlier, ill and in a great deal of pain from a raging appendicitis. Unfortunately the surgeon had not opened him up quite quickly enough, and the appendix had burst whilst in the process of removal, spilling its noxious contents along the way. With a good deal of suctioning and mopping and some large doses of penicillin, peritonitis had been averted and Richard was now well on the way to recovery.

"Can you remember the next line?" Margery had the wound, clean and well-healed, uncovered now and was rubbing off the sticky residue left by zinc oxide plaster with the help of 'Zoff' skin cleanser. She helped him out:

"The donkey shied and Daddy cried – "

"Inky Pinky Ponky," Richard finished triumphantly and giggled.

"I've got your operation uncovered now, Do you want to look?" Margery enquired.

"No." Richard quickly turned his head away.

"OK – no need, but I've got something very good to tell you!"

The head whipped back round. "What? Tell me now."

"I'll tell you in a minute; but first I have to take your stitches out."

The eyes widened in apprehension and Richard's head turned away again.

"Look at me, Richard," Margery was firm. "Taking stitches out DOES NOT HURT – providing you keep still. Now, what shall we sing? What about, 'There was an old man called Michael Finnigan?'"

Richard considered, still wary of what might happen in the next few minutes. "No," he decided. "Grandma's cat."

"Right," Margery began – "My Grandma's cat is black and he's fat," (snip, tweak one stitch out).

Richard, thinking about the next line, never flinched. "He looks like a cushion (snip, tweak, two) when sat on the mat."

"And sometimes at night (snip, tweak three) when he's feeling quite lazy," (snip, tweak) . . . The last line came out in a rush. It was a bit rude and therefore to be savoured:

"He wees on the carpet (snip tweak) – and Grandma goes crazy," (snip, tweak, all out).

What was it, Margery wondered, that, provided they didn't apply to themselves, made the words 'wee' and 'bottom' so hilariously funny to small children?

"Stitches done. Are you sure that you don't want to look now? It's quite pretty. A pink line with pink dots where the stitches have been. I'm going to cover it up again in a minute, and next time we look it will have nearly vanished."

Richard sneaked a tentative look at his operation scar and then favoured it with a more prolonged regard. "H'mm." No comment.

"Do you want to take your stitches home for Daddy to see?" Margery enquired, showing him the scraps of purple nylon thread that she'd carefully placed on a piece of gauze.

Yes, he would – and they were carefully stowed in his locker.

"Now, the good thing I promised to tell you." Margery was rooting in the locker for slippers and dressing gown. "You're getting up. Out of that bed with you! AND something even 'gooder'. Tomorrow if the doctor says 'yes' (and I think he will) you can go home!"

Margery left Richard sitting in a chair and pushed her dressing trolley into the clinic room for dismantling. Forceps, bowls and receivers into the steriliser for re-boiling, stitch scissors immersed in pure 'Lysol', all for re-use again when the need arose.

She must have a look, she mused, next time that she went home, for the book of nonsense rhymes she'd been given on her fifth birthday. It had given her pleasure then and could have a new lease of life now, fifteen years on. She returned to the ward and found that Richard had left his chair and was investigating a box of toys on the central carpet. Good.

When Richard's mum came to take him home on the following day, she sought Margery out. No effusive expressions of gratitude, no elaborate speeches, but her arms went out to Margery in an instinctive hug and there were just two words whispered in her ear. "Thank you." It was enough.

When a patient, adult or child, undergoes surgery for which a general anaesthetic is necessary, they were lifted straight from the operating table onto a trolley, still deeply unconscious and usually with a semi-rigid tube protruding from their lips. The purpose of this airway is in part to prevent the unconscious patient from swallowing his own tongue, a complication best avoided! On the trolley they are pushed by a porter and a junior nurse sent down for this purpose, back to the ward and received into a warm bed, there they are left to return slowly and naturally to the conscious world, observed informally by all the nursing staff busy toing and froing about their routine work. The immediate wakeful hours following surgery were not pleasant ones. Disorientation, vomiting, a raging thirst, and a sore throat – all unhappy results of the necessary anaesthetic. Then there is the operation itself. Extreme pain of 'innards', muscles and skin that have not just been handled, perhaps excessively so, but cut and stitched. Of course, pain relief is available once the patient is awake, which helps. All a bad enough experience for anyone, but horrendous for a child for whom one can add the fright of unfamiliar surroundings and the overwhelming desperate need for the comfort of their mother's presence.

Children's Ward were expecting three year old Diane back from theatre at any time. A bed was ready and waiting and soon a small comatose bundle, a black airway protruding from her mouth like an obscene 'dummy' appeared at the ward door. Covered with a blanket her small body needed only a portion of the adult-sized trolley on which she lay somehow making her seem especially vulnerable and pathetic.

As far as staffing allowed, Children's Ward Sister liked to have a nurse allocated to sit with an unconscious child until he or she became fully awake; there to monitor breathing, pulse, colour and, most importantly, obviate the possibility of vomit being inhaled – an ever present fear.

Margery welcomed the opportunity. Not only was it something of a luxury to be able to give one-to-one care to an individual, it was also a rest for tired feet – her own!

Diana had had an umbilical hernia repaired, a fairly routine operation – a hernia that probably owed its origin to before, during or shortly after her birth, when some of the abdominal contents had spilled through the aperture made by the soon to be redundant umbilical cord. Non-surgical attempts to right the hernia had proved unsuccessful and it had become necessary to 'stitch it back in' before it grew in size or caused other difficulties.

Margery checked her small patient's wound dressing – no bleeding – no discharge – pulse OK, and the little girl was breathing quietly, her colour returning.

Margery gazed round her. The child in the next bed, her broken thigh strapped to her good leg and both hoisted onto a wooden frame, was doing a jigsaw on her chest and talking to herself. With her head and chest flat on the bed and legs held up at a right angle, her body made a human L-shape – but it didn't seem to worry her unduly, and the jigsaw was coming along nicely. How infinitely adaptable some children are.

A series of plaques high up on the wall facing her caught Margery's eye. Part of the decoration, she'd never really looked at them in detail before, or considered their value. They depicted scenes from various nursery rhymes, executed in ceramic tiles and demonstrating a high degree of skill on the ceramicist's part. Works of art that would no doubt become valuable pieces of Victoriana in the future – but alas! – the detail was horrid. The hospital had been built in an era when it was thought acceptable to terrify children into good behaviour; when Hell and Damnation preachers stressed the vengeance of God, and before Walt Disney came along with his anthropomorphic mice and Mabel Lucie Attwell created her happy, chubby children.

Jack came tumbling down the hill, his broken crown gushing blood and brains. Interestingly Jill tumbled after him more sedately, arms and legs outstretched, but in spite of being upside down, her skirt remained securely unruffled and didn't expose her knees. That would have been too suggestive of things not appropriate for young minds to contemplate! Miss Muffet was running terror stricken from the spider – and no wonder! He glared malevolently with bared teeth, wickedness personified, from a head the size of a cauliflower. Margery remembered as a child disliking the black and white illustrations in a book of Grimm's fairy tales she had been given, and how she had turned over the pages quickly not liking the evil goblins and wicked witches she saw there. Now here was something similarly frightening with which to occupy children – and sick children to boot.

There was a whimper, a restless movement from the small figure beside her, Diane was wakening. Margery removed the airway from the child's mouth and lifted her head onto a pillow. Small, pathetic animal noises escaped, and then, "Hurts" and the inevitable wail for "Mummee". Margery retrieved the battered teddy, tidied away by whoever had made up the bed, and held child and teddy as well as she could, in her arms, making soothing noises and talking to the child quietly, aware that she might vomit and was too young and too bewildered to use the vomit bowl provided. Sister, seeing Diane's awakening, came with the required sedation. A needle, another whimper of misery and slowly sleep swallowed her up.

It would be two days till the next visiting day when Diane could see her beloved "Mummee" again. A lifetime for a three year old. The Victorians tormented their children with threats of the bogey man and his like, but we were still depriving them of their natural source of comfort, their mothers, when they were at their most needy – AND we still had the ceramic plaques. But then some humanitarian builder, plasterer or architect had seen fit to mount them so far up the wall that they were largely out of the range of children's eyes. Some mixed intentions there it would seem.

Margaret Woods was having her eyes well and truly opened. Not that situations new to her didn't occur at the hospital, they did just that, and one accommodated them as needed. However, the new eye opener was outside her daily round. Her fiancé, Roger, had completed his theological training, had been ordained, and was now one of three curates serving a large city centre parish in Liverpool. Margaret was spending her days off, when funds afforded the necessary fare, alongside him – doing pastoral visits and assisting in the night shelter that the church had set up in that very damaged city. She was seeing, at first-hand, the squalid circumstances that overcrowding created, the heartbreak of men discharged from the forces who came home to nothing; the acres of devastation which were slowly, oh so slowly, being cleared for re-building. Liverpool's docks and its railway network had been a magnet for Hitler's bombers seeking to cut off the island's food supplies, and Margaret clearly remembered seeing the red glow in the sky viewed from her home, some thirty miles away, and hearing her father's comment, "Liverpool's burning tonight."

Many, many houses were destroyed and their occupants killed. Violent and unwanted slum clearance some had called it, but slums were still homes and people had to live somewhere. Families that had a roof over their heads took in relatives and friends and were still doing so; people were living in cellars – the only part of once elegant houses remaining; in outhouses, old army huts and in air raid shelters. Bit by bit local authorities were moving towards the provision of tower blocks, new estates and even new towns. But these things took time, men were coming home and the baby boom was getting underway. Prefabs, a new innovation, were appearing, but still demand exceeded supply. Of course there was goodwill, togetherness and willingness to help each other. Charities like the British Legion, Red Cross and SSAFA, not to mention local churches as represented by Roger and his colleagues, were working to relieve the obvious difficulties of many. That there was also crime, corruption, profiteering, child neglect, ill health and ill-will was inevitable, and it was in this stew-pot of humanity that Roger spent his days trying, as he put it, to support people's lives, their bodies and their minds, and leaving their souls to God and Christian hope.

It was one day when Margaret was with a family who had just welcomed a new baby into their one-roomed 'flat', that she met an individual who was to give her fresh food for thought and perhaps influence her future professional development. There were already four people living in the one room and sleeping arrangements were extremely cramped. Margaret was trying to convince the mother that it would be safer for the new arrival to sleep in a cardboard box, or the bottom drawer of their one chest of drawers rather than in the communal bed that they all shared. Overlaying, in such a warm, but overcrowded bed was a definite possibility for such a young child, she had explained, when into the scenario came the local health visitor. Margaret had heard of such people but had little idea of their function. She soon found out. This lady, not a lot older than Margaret herself, was it seemed, an SRN with midwifery experience and a certificate in preventative medicine. A sort of nurse/social worker/teacher who was employed by the local authority. She checked on the new baby's general condition, reinforced Margaret's advice re sleeping arrangements and invited mother and baby to the Child Welfare Clinic adding, "And while you're with us, we'll see about some family planning. Yes? Think about it. Bring the kids – we've a supervised play area they can use whilst you're being seen."

This competent lady then turned her attention to the older children. She completed, with Mum's permission, the two year olds' immunisation schedule. A protest, a yell – no one likes needles – and then it was, "There, all done. No more till you start at school." A sweet was produced from her bag and she turned her attention to the six year old who had been watching the proceedings warily. "And where are your glasses?" she enquired. "I don't see them on your nose! You'll never be clever if you can't see the blackboard, you know."

"The frames are broken – again," Mother admitted. "I know she should wear them, but the other kids call her 'specky four eyes' and she puts them in her pocket and they get twisted." The health visitor sighed. Free eye tests and free glasses weren't much use if they weren't used. She took the glasses away with her – for free mending.

As Margaret walked down the hall, the rancid smell comprised of urine, sweat and yesterday's boiled cabbage caught in her throat. "Thank God," said the health visitor, "that the new babe is breast fed. Sterilising feeding bottles in these conditions is very difficult and that often means trouble."

Thank God. Yes, thank God, Margaret thought, for a mother

142

willing and able to breast feed in spite of her own not very robust health. Thank God for immunisation, for free glasses, and for a roof, of a kind, over the family's head. She must remember to thank God for what was provided and not just bemoan what was so fundamentally lacking.

So many disordered, dysfunctional lives exacerbated by Hitler's attentions, but mainly deriving from ignorance, greed, tradition and expedience; conditions that underlie so much ill health both physical and mental.

The health visitor's role, based on the short glimpse afforded to Margaret, was an interesting one, the certificate in preventative medicine, a possibility worth considering. 'Prevention is better than cure' was a truism applying just as much here in England's smelly armpit as amongst the foreign faces of – wherever. She must talk this through with Roger. . .

Ophthalmic Ward. A six week spell here was all part of the grand plan, and one by one the students did their stint there, finding it on the whole the most boring, or perhaps more accurately, the least exciting, ward in the hospital. Twelve male and twelve female beds and a small theatre used specifically for eye surgery was the exclusive domain of the ward sister.

How different was the work here. Generally speaking the ward catered for mainly elderly patients needing cataract surgery and there were many of these. Such an operation, before the advent of the NHS, was outside the means of many people and few were performed. Also occupying a fair proportion of the beds were children needing squints corrected. An eclectic mix. Of course there were other cases to leaven the load. Detached retinas needing re-fixing, a difficult and not always successful procedure, acute glaucomas and the inevitable eye injuries. November 5th with its fireworks and bonfires was back on the agenda of people's lives after years of black-out. Excited children picked up and peered into fireworks that they thought defunct, only to have them ignite into their enquiring faces.

Memories of working on eye ward were usually of the endless hours, with both eyes bandaged, that the older patients, 'the cataracts' spent. Lying flat and avoiding sudden movements, or effort of any kind, for about two weeks. As if this wasn't ordeal enough they had already endured a two hour operation under a local anaesthetic with their head fixed in a sort of frame to keep it immobile – but Hallelujah! the operation came free of charge, with three meals a day thrown in, and IF it was successful they might be rewarded with the pleasure of being able to see their grandchildren.

If a stay on ophthalmic ward was a trial of patience for 'the cataracts' how much more difficult it was for the children who also had both their eyes covered with bandages when recovering from their strabismus (squint) corrections. After the effects of the general anaesthetic had worn off, these children, temporarily deprived of sight, didn't feel ill and keeping them amused, happy and reasonably still was the gargantuan task of the nursing staff who read to them, found them tactile puzzles and encouraged conversation with fellow sufferers. No play leaders, special teachers – not even a radio. A bad squint in one or both eyes so impairs vision that such children are categorised as 'partially sighted', a condition that can blight their education and their lives generally. Also, of course, a severe squint is unsightly earning children ridicule and teasing from their peers, so the operation was considered well worth the effort and patience involved, and was usually successful.

Margery didn't feel it was fair. . . She had been on Eye Ward for five weeks and was dismayed at the lack of information given to the cataract patients regarding their eye condition and what they might expect from surgery. The eye surgeon, a man of few words, did not deem explanations were necessary and was unwilling to discuss outcomes. He would operate and, in the fullness of time, it was hoped that some sight would be restored, and the less said about it the better. The whole episode, for the patient, was a journey into the unknown beset with unrealistic expectations and imperfect understanding of their problem. For many the miracle of restored sight was touched with drama not unknown and, to some extent instigated, by Hollywood. How different was the reality.

So Margery took it upon herself, whilst performing the usual tasks – washing, toileting, bed making and helping with meals, to correct a few misconceptions. "No," she told her patients, there would be no ceremony wherein the surgeon would remove their bandages and pronounce success, retiring with the plaudits of assembled staff and relatives ringing in his ears. There would be no flooding of the room with sunshine and, she added to herself, Sister would not be in the background sawing away on a violin she happened to have with her!

Margery explained gently that they, in the immediate future, could expect little improvement in their sight but that this would come when spectacles had been supplied. The general belief was that a film had grown over their eyes which had to be removed when it was 'ready' – that is when it was substantial enough to grasp. Margery's explanation that the lens of their eyes had been removed because they had become 'milky' and opaque was something of a revelation. Not everyone was even aware that glasses would always have to be worn to replace the missing lens. Margery felt justified in her efforts to avert the disappointment of no immediate restoration of clarity of vision, but uncomfortable with and uncertain of assuming responsibility for this, her attempts at patient education. These patients, she felt, may not have the specialist knowledge of the medical world, but they were not unintelligent and deserved better. No, it wasn't fair.

It was not often these days that the six remaining members of the October '48 PTS all got together in one place. Working on different wards, off duty times rarely coincided, so it was something unusual for them to be exclusively in one another's company. They'd worked until 8pm, had supper and were now spread at ease in front of the sitting room fire. Month end was approaching, so no one had any money and those that were fancy-free, no 'dates'.

"Quite like old times at Albert Terrace," Jane remarked. "Shouldn't someone be washing their hair?"

"That", said Margery, "was about a million years ago. What I want to know is – why are patients so left in the dark about their own conditions and treatment?"

"Oh, Lord," Jane groaned. "We are not going to have a deeply philosophical debate on the ethics and practice of medicine are we? Pseudo religious and psychologically ill-informed as we are."

"My religion is not pseudo," said Margaret mildly, "and my psychology, little as it is, is based on observations made on the ground and not taken from text books."

"Well, I'm too tired for such deep and clever thinking," said Jane, and went to bed.

g

"You're right though," this was from Audrey. "They, that is the patients, on the whole accept what happens to them without question, believing that the doctor or nurse knows what is best for them even when 'what's best' is unpleasant. The body and how it works is an unknown and what goes on under the skin a mystery for others to understand. It can be almost, but not quite, comical at times. Yesterday I heard a patient ask a doctor what was in the tablets she was taking and how they would help her. Do you know, he stared at her in surprise for a moment, and then said – 'What's it got to do with you?' – a perfectly genuine question from an efficient and hard working medical man."

This was a long speech, coming from Audrey who was not given to much social interchange, but she too obviously felt uncomfortable with the 'them' – the patients and 'us' – the professionals dichotomy.

Audrey giggled. "Like – it's my job to prescribe the pill, the nurse's job to hand it out and your job is to swallow it. End of story."

"Mm-m, but seriously," Margery persisted, "if a person understands his disease and the nature of its treatment that must help recovery, mustn't it?"

"We-ell, I'm not sure everyone would want to know. Some would – and can ask. . . Others might like to ask but would think that they wouldn't understand, and may look foolish." Eileen, who had been dozing in a corner of the settee suddenly roused and thought of her mother's reverential attitude towards the family GP who she thought of as a 'very clever man'. An attitude that rendered her so overwhelmed by his presence and superior knowledge that she wouldn't dream of questioning his opinion and advice.

"Why, for instance," Margery continued, "are patients' notes only available exclusively to medical and nursing staff and not to the person most concerned. They are kept in the office, which is most inconvenient, so that the danger of patients reading about their own illness is averted!"

"It's a bit pointless 'cos they wouldn't understand what they read – I can't half the time." Anne had no qualms about displaying her own failings. "a) the handwriting is impossible b) they use initials, abbreviations and acronyms all the time and c) half the words (that is IF they are readable) would mean nothing.

It's all part of maintaining the medical mystique, a secret language known only to the enlightened few. To be shared with favoured colleagues alone. It's written into the Hypocritical Oath you know."

"Hippocratic – you ignorant twit."

Anne grinned. "I know, but what I don't know is – do doctors at some point actually swear it, with their hands on their hearts – you know – like Americans do when they sing *The Star Spangled Banner*. Does it exist, chiselled into a lump of stone somewhere, or is it a comfortable myth?"

"Dunno, I think Hippocrates came later, and they had papyrus."

"Oh," Margery gave this some thought. "But I'm sure I've heard, or read, or been told that this oath, whether real or mythical, covers mainly the promise to keep the profession exclusive, and to guard well one's superior knowledge, barring it to outsiders; And that healing the sick, easing pain and preserving life is thrown in as an afterthought. Do you think that's true?"

"Dunno."

"There seems to be a lot we 'Dunno'. This conversation is going nowhere , so I'm to bed. Good night."

One by one the group wandered off, leaving Audrey alone. 'Acronyms' she mused and gave a mental smile at an incident that had occurred on her last visit home. A neighbour had come in carrying the 'sick note' acquired by her daughter and intended for her employer. The note informed him that the girl was unfit by reason of URTI. Could Audrey tell her if this was serious? Should she be worried? No one seemed to have heard of such a disease. URTI, Audrey had explained, stood for Upper Respiratory Tract Infection. Her daughter had a cold.

The secret language revealed! And Audrey too went to bed.

Chapter Eleven

Is there, has there ever been, will there ever be, a more tasteless, unappealing, bland, boring and – well – plain squelchy item of food than a vegetable marrow? It was September, and this ubiquitous vegetable was appearing with monotonous frequency on the plates of the residents at Merton Royal Infirmary who required two nutritious meals a day. The kitchen supervisor had not yet devised a method of serving it up for breakfast, but it must be said his innovations for dinner and supper menus were nothing short of enterprising. Marrow appeared covered in white sauce at dinner time, stuffed with forcemeat or blanketed with cheese at supper time, and even in an attempt to vary the 'milk-ur-sponge' choice for desert, flavoured with lemon juice, dipped in batter, fried, and dusted off with icing sugar. Wow!

"Is there any food value whatsoever in this stuff, do you think?" Jane was picking its stuffing out and pushing the marrow to one side.

"Probably vitamins and minerals, though I've never heard of any." Anne was forking it into her ever-ready mouth. "Anyway, it's excellent roughage, so eat it up like a good girl. It's good for your bowels."

"There's nothing wrong with my bowels, thank you," Jane grumbled and went off to her room where she had a packet of potato crisps – they would stave off the hunger pangs till breakfast, and soon this marrow-fest would be over – until next year.

The cause of this marrow-mania and these culinary difficulties was the universal practice of the many churches in and around the town to each celebrate a harvest festival; a festival that gave praise and thanks to the Almighty for his yearly munificence.

"We plough the fields and scatter, the good seed on the land," sang the worthy parishioners, whether they lived in terraced housing cheek by jowl with the mills and their chimneys in the town, or in a 'semi-detached' in the suburbs. "All is safely gathered in," – and gather it in they did, decorating their churches, and then distributing their offerings to the poor and needy.

Regrettably, marrows can be grown in back yards in pots, as well as in more traditional gardens. Lancashire's damp climate suited their development; their size and abundance epitomised fertility and plenty. Digging for Victory had been a government mantra for years and so marrows continued to be produced and delivered to the churches for decoration. The trouble was that the recipients of this bounty – the 'poor and needy' – really didn't want the things, even when so generously given. So the marrows came – where else – to the local hospital. Old habits, that of supporting the local hospital with money, with effort and in kind, die hard, as does the practice of *never* wasting food, so patients and staff ate marrow. Ad infinitum.

As September melted into October, the days shortened and November 5th brought its usual crop of sparks in eyes, burnt fingers and this year, a child who had eaten half a roman candle. His distraught mother, expecting him to explode at any minute had doused him in water and brought him into Casualty shivering with cold but otherwise unaffected. The nurses were accustomed to elderly patients with constipation asking for 'gun-powder' to ease their difficulties – but at the age of three the actual stuff appeared to have little effect!

As December arrived and Christmas began to be anticipated in the town's shops, an exciting new possibility emerged led by the recently appointed head pharmacist. He and his wife were prominent members of the town's drama society, a long established amateur organisation with its own playhouse and a reputation and following to rival more professional entertainers.

Mr Fellows was a talented amateur pianist and his wife an actress of local repute. Together they conceived the notion of putting on a concert at the hospital for staff, management, and patients to enjoy at Christmas.

The idea was received with enthusiasm, mainly by the nurses. Those members of staff who 'lived out' and hadn't the same commitment to the life of the hospital in its broadest sense, were less keen, but a few joined in, and a programme was devised. They would base their entertainment, it was decided, on the music of shows having current success in London. *Annie get your Gun*, *Oklahoma* and *South Pacific*.

Oh, the music, the extravagance, the joy of those shows, contrasting so favourably with the economies and greyness of post-war Britain. They were American, of course, but then for years America had assumed a sort of folk image compounded of the romantic wild west and a land of plenty where ration books and clothing coupons were unknown.

Mr Fellows proved a competent producer, in spite of all the traumas of finding a cast that could sing in tune and execute simple dance steps. Then there was the problem of costumes and that of rehearsals. When every hour of the twenty-four and each of the seven days of the week demanded a nursing presence on the wards, the poor man was reduced to holding rehearsals at which the full cast were never present – after all, someone had to 'mind the shop'.

The finale of the show was to be a can-can line up of the six most curvaceous nurses ready and willing to high kick with enthusiasm. After all, they already had the black stockings, and the rest of the outfit (including the frilly panties) would, they were told, arrive in good time. . .

When the costumes did arrive they turned out to be not the glamorous confections hoped for, but several bolts of pink and green taffeta. Mrs Fellows produced a simple dress pattern and demonstrated how to make frills by running gathering stitches along strips of material and sewing them in rows across the seats of Marks and Spencer's knickers. The ladies from the sewing room volunteered their expertise (it made a welcome change from the eternal patching and darning of bed linen) and mothers and sisters were pressed into service. Where the taffeta had come from remained a mystery.

Eventually a quite respectable company of singers and dancers, all resplendent in pink and green, was assembled to Mr and Mrs Fellows satisfaction. They were ready.

It was then that the bombshell fell. The doctors had also been secretly rehearsing and would like to present two humorous sketches as their contribution to the entertainment. The nurses were delighted, Mr Fellows less so. Medical humour, as he knew full well, could be bawdy. Jokes often named parts of the body not usually mentioned in respectable society – goodness knows he'd joined in and guffawed with the rest in the past. But in front of Matron, the hospital management committee and the patients?

"No," said the doctors, "they hadn't the time to run through their efforts beforehand. He would have to trust them."

Christmas Day began as it had done, traditionally, for years, with carol singing on the wards. Nurses were roused at 5am, furnished with a red-lined cape, a lantern and a carol sheet, and be-caped and be-capped, a crocodile led by Matron wound its way round each ward. *Christians Awake* and *O Come all ye Faithful* lustily rang out and was apparently, if later comments were to be believed much appreciated by those individuals well enough to register it. Then came the once a year treat for the carollers. Bacon *and* egg for breakfast.

The rest of the day passed in an agony of nerves for the performers, but at last the nurses sitting room (which was large and boasted a stage at one end) was made ready and the audience started to arrive. The front row was reserved for Matron and the hospital management committee, then came a row of wheel chairs as patients were brought down suitably tucked into blankets, and at the back, all ready to cheer, boo, shout or cat-call as the mood took them – were the staff. They crammed into a space much too small for their numbers but it all added to the fun. Even Sam turned up, looking unfamiliar in his best suit.

As might be expected, the concert opened with a rendering of *Another Opening, Another Show* and this was followed by a humorous monologue performed by Mrs Fellows. More choruses and a couple of simple dance routines and then the audience was invited to join in with *It's a Grand Night for Singing*. These efforts were encouraged by 'a guest conductor of great eminence' – the orthopaedic registrar conducting with a patella hammer in place of a baton. The first half concluded with Sister Fortune's solo *When I marry Mr Snow*. It brought the house down. The offers to "Forget Mr Snow and marry me love," and similar comments came thick and fast. Whatever the show lacked in sophistication, it was made up for with exuberant audience participation.

After the break (cups of tea in the dining room) came the long anticipated offerings by the medical staff. Mr Fellows held his breath. The curtains opening with the well-known sound, played fortissimo, of 'stripper' music. Centre stage a hospital screen hid some sort of activity unseen but easily imagined. In perfect time to the music a hand appeared brandishing a black lace bra. This was flung into the audience, landing, amongst cheers, on Matron's lap. Some frilly panties followed, which hit the chairman amidships, a suspender belt and then some black stockings fluttered down. The audience loved it! Eventually, as the music reached its expected climax, the screen was whipped away to reveal a six foot beefy gentleman in furry bedroom slippers and a wrap around floral apron straining over a very prominent bosom. He/she was busy doing the family ironing.

After that little extravaganza the audience couldn't wait for number two. Mr Fellows launched into some manual gymnastics on the piano to fill the gap, and the curtain rose on, this time, a park bench and a rather wonky street light. This had obviously been fashioned from an intra-venous drip stand with a cardboard lantern on top in which a torch covered in red cellophane glimmered feebly. Enter, right, an individual in a blonde wig of startling hue. He/she had a tight off the shoulder top (oh! the size and rotundity of the bosom) a short satin skirt and high heels, the latter doing little for the hairy and muscular legs above them. Amid cheers from the audience, he/she wiggled and posed, eyelashes batting madly at the chairman who was thoroughly enjoying himself on the front row. Enter, left, a small grey man in a long mac, looking furtive and guilty. The wiggles, the invitation grew more and more blatant until eventually the 'punter' produced his wallet and offered money. This was refused – not enough. More blandishments more enticing poses and more money was offered – still not enough. Eventually at the third offer the 'lady' accepted, gave a quick nod and exited, at which her customer, grinning broadly, picked up the bench and left in the opposite direction. Curtain, and Mr Fellows relaxed.

Six slim and attractive girls high kicking across the stage with plenty of energy if not professional precision couldn't fail to bring the show to a triumphant conclusion. The audience beat time and can-canned vocally, there being no room to do otherwise, and cheered them on and on, until fearing total exhaustion and collapse the curtain was closed. As the performers gathered for their final bow the doctor from the first 'stripper' sketch stepped forward. Expecting the usual speech of thanks to the producer, the audience quietened. Not so. He stepped down from the stage and, addressing the chairman directly, asked "Please, sir, can I have my knickers back?"

The anticlimax of January wasn't helped by darkly freezing weather. Orthopaedic ward filled up with ladies who had fractured their hips falling in the slippery outdoors and surgeons were kept busy inserting Smith-Peterson pins into their broken bones. For years a broken neck of femur (hip) had meant a future life of invalidism in bed or at best in a wheelchair and it was with difficulty that the nurses persuaded these patients that they must sit up (lest hypostatic pneumonia finished them off) and within quite a short time get out of bed and start walking again. Shock, horror from concerned relatives that these hard hearted nurses and physiotherapists were expecting mother to WALK. Didn't they understand that she had a BROKEN HIP? Alas, the progress of medical science and the consideration of long term results had passed them by.

It was hard to believe that the girls were now third year students and regularly left in charge of a ward, and that at the end of this year they would be facing their final exams. But first there was a period of a minimum six weeks spent as operating theatre staff, a stint in Accident and Emergency, and a night duty in charge of a major ward. There might even be, for some, a 'rest cure', that is a period at one or other of the three convalescent homes; adjuncts to the main hospital and now known by their new name – continuation hospitals. Here the work was light, the food excellent and the general ambience more relaxed, but many found the isolation from their peers hard to tolerate.

Meanwhile there was a life outside the hospital. Margaret continued to spend her days off at her fiancés side, passing the night not very comfortably on a camp bed provided by Roger's landlady. He was lucky in his 'digs', through the personality of this lady who 'did for' the curates at the local church. Once Roger had persuaded her to stop addressing him as Father (she was a good forty years his senior), they rubbed along fine. Mrs O'Leary was a good Irish Catholic (but sure, we'll not worry about that Father – I mean Roger) and a good cook. She welcomed Margaret's visits, and Margaret the improved diet. The great four-year plan continued.

Eileen, the other member of the group whose affections were already decided, was anticipating change, and was daring to think of a wedding in early 1952. Kevin had almost completed his time as a National Serviceman and would be coming home shortly. He had plans to set up his own business in the motor trade, but the difficulties seemed endless. Where would they live? What would they live *on* until he got established? Where would they find the money to start him off? But, there, if that's what Kevin aspired to do, Eileen would go along with it. She knew perfectly well that Merton Royal Infirmary didn't consider its nurses to be fully trained until they had worked as a staff nurse for twelve months after the state had awarded its registration and that Matron wouldn't employ a married nurse; that she would never wear the hospital training badge if she didn't complete the twelve months as a staff nurse; that she would have to work and earn, in the early years of marriage, and above all that she was desperate to consummate their partnership legally and properly with a white wedding and all the trimmings that went with it. Above this uncertain future hung the final state exam. Not for the first time Eileen wanted to run away and cry in frustration, but if she did that the last two years would have been for nothing. Who wanted a partly trained nurse? Nobody who knew what was what. She would, she decided, concentrate on passing her finals, by no means a forgone conclusion, and then decide whether or not to defy Matron and find a job elsewhere. Meanwhile there was no harm in gazing in the windows of shops selling wedding dresses, was there?

Of the other four members of the October '48 intake, Audrey continued to go her own way, disappearing home on her day off and adding little to social intercourse in the group. Margery, still fancy free, enjoyed the odd date, visits to the cinema, a game of tennis perhaps, a Saturday 'hop'. Standing on a freezing sideline watching someone else play football was not her idea of a good afternoon's entertainment and several young men that had at first

154

seemed personable soon got the push if that was what they expected of her.

Jane? Jane was in love with a horse. She had acquired this animal, a sprightly grey mare by the name of Silver Streak some weeks ago and had her stabled only a 2d bus ride away from the hospital at a local farm. Presumably Daddy's hand had gone into his pocket in effecting the purchase. With a salary that amounted, after deductions, to less than £5.00 per month, Jane's acquisition could hardly have been by her own funding. Now she spent every spare moment feeding, grooming and exercising Silver. The horse was her pride and joy. She entered, when she could, the various gymkhanas and other competitive shows that the local 'horsey' set put on, and was quite successful. Successful enough to aspire to greater things, and there it seemed lay the difficulty. She only knew, as they all did, a week in advance which hours they would be required to work. Even then the time off could be changed at a moment's notice if pressure of work decreed. First, last and every time the needs of the hospital prevailed, and always would. The social lives of the staff came second if they were considered at all, which made any outside activity fraught with difficulty.

Which left Anne. Plump, pretty, willing and witty and always, always ready for a joke, Anne was embroiled in a torrid love affair with a married man a good deal older than herself. Anne made no secret of the fact that for both of them, the objective was sex. Wonderful, exciting, illicit, inventive coupling wherever and whenever the opportunity arose. For her a revelation, for him, with a string of similar affairs behind him, a refreshing change.

This activity was viewed by her colleagues according to their various natures with disapproval (nice girls just DIDN'T), curiosity, interest, worry (she'll get pregnant) and by them all, with concern. She was their friend. They had lived with her, worked with her, she was fun, they liked her and she was going to get hurt. Margery, ever rational, asked – in view of the cold grey conditions outside – "Where do you – well – do it?"

Anne was nonchalant, "Back seat of a borrowed car, a friend's flat, an empty carriage on the way back from Blackpool. . ." Evidently where there was a will, there was a way.

"How sordid, how unromantic, uncomfortable, grubby."

"Yes," said Anne, quite unrepentant, "but it's worth it." The inference being – what do any of you know about such things?

155

She was going to grab what she could of pleasure in a life that she found restricting, emotionally wearing, physically tiring and condemned her to near poverty. She wasn't daft, knew it wouldn't last and was going nowhere. Meanwhile she was hurting no one, so – carpe diem.

Anne had met Gee briefly when he had visited his mother in the hospital, and met him again, by chance, on the top of a bus travelling into town. He invited her to have a drink with him and she found that he was the landlord of a town centre pub and enjoyed a limited amount of notoriety as an ex-professional footballer who had played for the local team. In a football mad town like Merton that amounted to fame, and there were many who remembered his exploits on the field with nostalgia. Gee's pub did not rank with the few notorious establishments in the town that commanded attention from the police on a regular basis, but was nevertheless, rough. That is, noisy, beery and smoky and not the sort of place one took the wife for a comfortable drink on a Saturday night.

At one time Gee had been selected for the England Squad, but sadly had never got further than the substitutes bench. However, he made the most of it with relevant cuttings from the *Lancashire Evening Post* framed behind the bar.

Also behind the bar was Mrs Gee. A competent lady who viewed her husband's infidelities with tolerant indifference – she had her own life. She organised the staff, cellar men, glass washers and table clearers, kept the accounts, communicated with the brewery, and was in effect the landlord in all but name. Gee? He pulled the odd pint and chatted with the clientele – his opinion on matters of football still sought – and eased himself comfortably through the life that the pub gave him.

By March the affair was waning. Anne took the growing signs of disinterest philosophically, and if the truth were told was becoming less enthralled herself.

Then wham! Things were brought to a head, or perhaps an end might be more accurate, by Mrs Gee departing for pastures new – taking the current week's takings with her. She left behind a set of scrupulously kept accounts and a letter to the brewery explaining that the amount she felt she was owed in past salary was now safely in her pocket. Her husband she ignored.

By June, without a controlling hand the pub was failing, and then later that summer, long after the Gee and Anne affair had petered out, the brewery moved in and it was goodbye to livelihood, home and wife.

"Life is like that," Anne said.

"No, no, no," said Margaret.

"Not inevitably," said Eileen.

"Depends what you make of it," declared Margery.

"Prefer animals," from Jane, and Audrey said nothing. It was over.

"Have you seen the new assistant pharmacist?" my goodness he's gorgeous. Stewart Granger and Ray Milland rolled into one." Anne enthused.

Her friends breathed a collective sigh of relief. This was normal, this was natural, this was healthy. . . then in all their minds came the same thought, voiced for once by Audrey. "Is he married?"

Chapter Twelve

Abortion. The dictionary defines it as 'the ending before completion of a time-limited enterprise'. So, taken literally, any activity can be subject to abortion if it is proving to be unwanted or unsatisfactory and by any means that are suitable and available. In most people's minds, however, the word abortion applies virtually exclusively to the deliberate terminating of a pregnancy before its gestational nine months have expired. The word carried connotations of illegal practices, performed by unqualified persons in less than ideal conditions, for money. Back-street abortionists still existed in 1950, alive and well and selling their criminal services to any young woman desperate enough, and having the required sum of money, to submit to their attentions.

In the world of medicine and the parlance of its personnel, any woman admitted to hospital by reason of a threatened miscarriage was diagnosed as an abortion; such individuals sub-divided into TAs (threatened abortions) and IAs (inevitable abortions). That some of these patients had indeed, by their own efforts, or that of others, attempted to destroy their unborn child, was no doubt true, but for many patients the use of the word 'abortion' in relation to themselves was distressing in the extreme. Their babies were very much wanted, and their situation one of anxiety and fear for their as yet unborn child. Sadly, though the word is avoidable, its use was, and possibly still is, very much a widespread practice.

It was, of course, possible under very stringent guidelines to obtain a 'medical abortion', a procedure rarely undertaken (and never at Merton Royal Infirmary) involving as it did ethical and legal issues, the teachings and direction of the Church, and the surgeon's own views on what amounted to the taking of life. The 'never at Merton Royal' embargo was that of Consultant Gynaecologist, Mr Corby. A good practising Catholic, his word was law, and so general practitioners feeling that a patient of theirs was in need of such an intervention, sent them 20 or 30 miles away to a hospital where a surgeon of more liberal views might be found.

Where Grandpa Corby's views were crumbling slightly was in the field of contraception. He was fully aware that the nursing staff offered advice, instruction and the provision of cervical caps, diaphragms and sheaths – the only gadgetry available at the time – and chose to ignore their efforts. More significant was the provision of surgical contraception, known colloquially as 'getting your tubes tied'. He jibbed at doing this himself but allowed his Registrar to 'tie the knots', providing there were good medical reasons for doing so, of course.

There was no doubt about it; everyone knew it, saw it, fantasised about its cause. Sister Bennett did not like 'abortions' on her ward. At any one time there would be two or three of these ladies occupying beds on Alexandra Ward each with the pains and fears of their fellow patients and in addition suffering the emotional trauma of loss, or fear of loss. The good sister's pride in her work and her professionalism would not allow her patients to be neglected in any way, but her attitude towards those in danger of loss was cool and distant. She avoided all but basic, monosyllabic conversation with both them and their relatives, and positively encouraged the medical staff to discharge them home as soon as possible.

Why? Some thought that perhaps the sister had had a similar tragedy in her own marriage and that these patients brought back unhappy memories. Others that the incompatibility between her patients' needs and the voice of the law was the problem. The law and the church, and the views of celibate priests as interpreted by Mr Corby, a bachelor himself. It was all just too bewildering, so let's get these ladies back on their feet – and home.

Third year. Last year as a student nurse and night duty loomed again. Now the 'gang of six' had considerable responsibilities to maintain, each in charge of a major ward with one or sometimes two juniors to manage. The learning curve was a steep one. Coping with the many variances of an acute ward, and always expecting the unexpected, was part of the process, the climb towards more knowledge and practice. Margaret Woods found herself in charge of the largest ward in the hospital, Medical, with two juniors to assist. Eileen also had two juniors to help her manage Children's Ward and Margery, Anne and Audrey were each allocated an acute surgical ward with one 'helper' each.

Jane? Jane found herself directed to Alexandra Ward where she was to have her first taste of gynaecology and of the Sister Bennett experience.

From what she had heard from others, the night nurse in charge was certainly expected to maintain the high standards practised during the day, so it was with some trepidation that Jane opened the day report book, meticulously filled with Sister B's precise phraseology and neat handwriting.

Luckily Jane's junior nurse, a Nurse Jackson, known as Jackie was coming to the end of her three months night duty and knew the routine and where all the equipment was kept. For the first few nights roles were, in part, reversed as she initiated Jane into the night's work.

There were advantages to be had in working on Alexandra Ward. Very few deaths, or such desperately ill patients that relatives had to be accommodated, and very few, compared to other acute wards, emergency admissions. There were the threatened abortions of course; twisted ovarian cysts often admitted as acute appendices and normally transferred to Alexandra Ward when the misdiagnosis was confirmed. Then there were the ectopic pregnancies – a fairly rare condition whereby a fertilised egg starts to develop in the tube running from the ovary, instead of in its proper place, safely in the womb. Most patients arrived on the ward as their names came to the top of a waiting list. A good nurse did well to remember that these were not just another hysterectomy, another prolapse needing repair – one of the many passing through – but individuals whose arrival marked for them a huge event that they had anticipated with fear and dread, as well as the hope of some relief. A 'life event' that would count, along with child birth as a measure of the passage of time. 'Before my operation' or 'since my operation' came for many to mean a date from which they calculated other events, disasters and triumphs. Old wives' tales abounded. Loss of femininity, of libido, a life of invalidism – so that often patients arrived ignorant of what was in store for them and beset with doubts and fears that hopefully they would find groundless.

There were also disadvantages to working on night duty because of the extra tasks delegated to the night staff and intended to satisfy Sister Bennett's need for order and efficiency. One of these tasks was the counting and recording of all items of cutlery used on the ward. Convinced that cutlery was going missing, Sister B required that every item, from teaspoons to serving spoons, knives, forks and the rest be accounted for, and a cutlery book signed to say all were present and correct. If this wasn't so, a weary search for perhaps one missing teaspoon had to be made and, embarrassingly, patients quizzed as to the contents of their lockers. That anyone should wish to take home a piece of the hospital's very utilitarian cutlery, each piece stamped with the words 'Merton Royal Infirmary', seemed highly unlikely. A souvenir on a par with the presents brought back from holiday of the 'A present from Blackpool' variety? Surely not.

On the whole, Jane found Sister Bennett surprisingly benign and had reason, following an incident on the ward, to appreciate the lady's understanding of the shock and horror that at times rocked even the most experienced individual's equilibrium.

Saturday evening, the ward had settled down hopefully for a quiet night. In fact, Jane had actually brought a jumper she was knitting on duty with her, for with no operating list for the morrow, Sunday, perhaps there might be a hiatus in the continual cutting and folding of gauze swabs that normally filled the small hours, and she could employ the time otherwise. A young woman, Miss Dolores Taylor, had been admitted around 7pm that evening and diagnosed as an inevitable abortion. On examination no heart beat could be heard and she was losing blood-stained amniotic fluid – a bad omen. The patient was unforthcoming about her history. Unco-operative; couldn't, or wouldn't, say how long she had been pregnant, had had no ante natal care and suffered no recent unusual events, such as a fall, that might have precipitated her condition. She admitted having felt no movements from

161

inside her womb for 'ages' and though what she thought had been labour pains had started two days ago, they had 'gone off'. A frightened flat mate, alarmed at the bleeding, had sent for an ambulance and here she was – unhappy, truculent and apparently unaware of her own precarious condition. The gynie registrar decided on a 'wait and see policy' for the next few hours, and as the night staff arrived she was sleeping peacefully in a small side room off the main ward. So far, so good.

It was when Jane had sent off her junior for her midnight break that she decided she would walk round to each bed, checking this and that, and doing what she could to aid those patients who were not sleeping. Night Sister's round was not for another couple of hours and if everything was OK then she might get on with her knitting.

It was soon apparent that everything was far from OK. The girl in the side room was panting and perspiring, her body heaving with what appeared to be strong rhythmic pains. She gasped and whimpered, clinging onto the head of the bed with both hands. For a moment Jane stilled with horror, so very aware of her own lack of knowledge. She had never seen a baby born, knew only vaguely of a midwife's role; according to the day report this baby was probably dead, and Jane found herself hoping that this was so. One couldn't do harm, in one's own ineptitude, to a dead baby. But what of the mother? Jane was quite alone, no one but other patients within shouting distance. Should she run to the phone and summon Night Sister – that is if she could find her. She might be anywhere in the hospital and the Tannoy system wasn't in use at night. The decision was made for her by the patient, who released her hold on the bed head and gripped Jane's forearm with an iron hand, begging, "Don't leave me – please don't leave me.".

"I won't," Jane promised and pulled back the bed covers with her free hand. No splashes of scarlet, thank goodness, but emerging from between the patient's thighs was what looked like a dirty tennis ball. Jane knew that most babies are born head first. Perhaps she should help it out? To Jane's unpractised eye the vagina looked impossibly stretched and in danger of splitting. . . and Dolores was now howling with ghastly animal noises of fear and distress. With a heave and an almost involuntary lurch the baby's head was born, and Jane, rigid with horror and revulsion,

162

realised it was just that. A head but with no body attached. Jane's immediate thought was that the mother must not be allowed to see this ultimate nightmare that had emerged from her body, so she pushed the head down towards its mother's feet and untucked the bottom sheet pulling it over the baby's head.

With the head born, a few minutes respite from effort gave Dolores a short rest before, with another heave, a bloody tangle of rubbery looking white sticks and a mess of partly decomposed flesh and entrails erupted onto the bed. The smell was obscene. The patient, now relieved of her burden, was lying back and breathing normally. Jane took her pulse. A bit fast but strong and steady. Fighting nausea she considered what next she should do. Clear up the mess? Instinct told her it must be preserved, but going to collect receptacles meant leaving the girl to contemplate the noxious heap that had once been a living entity with a hope of independent life. Again the decision was made for her, by the welcome return of Jackie whose cheerful face appearing round the door, soon changed to one of consternation and shock.

"Get Sister quickly," Jane's voice trembled now help was in sight, "then bring a bucket with a lid."

Night Sister, recognising the urgency in Jackie's voice, was quick to respond. She summoned a doctor, warned the theatre nurse to prepare for an emergency D & C, then helped Jane to change the bed, wash the now exhausted Dolores and put her into a theatre gown. The baby went into the bucket.

It wasn't until the patient had been wheeled off to theatre, there to ensure that the uterus was indeed empty, that reaction to the whole episode set in, and Jane began to shake. Her teeth chattered and she shivered and shook, going to the kitchen and leaning against the radiator for warmth. Still cold, she left the kitchen and made her way to the large, walk-in, linen cupboard, Sister Bennett's pride and joy, and crept into its comforting warmth. There she hugged herself in its friendly darkness and gradually the shaking ceased. Guilt at the thought of Jackie out there doing the work of two people drove her to pull herself together. Her face was wet from a runny nose, streaming eyes, and of course, she couldn't find her handkerchief. Don't hankies always vanish when you need one? So she took a clean pillow slip from the shelf above her head and blew her nose, mopping herself dry.

When she emerged, the first person she saw was the Roman

163

Catholic Chaplain. Of course, she had forgotten it was Sunday and that several patients had expressed the wish to receive Holy Communion. So there he was, in his priestly robes and bearing the bread and the wine. Jane was relieved to find that the efficient Jackie had covered the relevant bedside lockers with a white cloth, found vases of flowers and drawn the bed curtains. Whilst the priest was doing his stuff, Jane returned to the kitchen and made herself a cup of tea and a jam sandwich, the only food the ward kitchen could provide. And considered.

She had, on previous occasions, found it necessary, at a relative's request to send for a priest to deliver the last rites to a dying patient. Sometimes, arriving too late, they, the priests that is, had spent some time with the corpse. Were you given the 'last rites' if you were already dead? Jane didn't know – but if one did, ought not an unborn child be afforded the same attention? Perhaps she should ask.

Father Phillips was a cheerful young man, popular with the staff and ready to hold out the hand of friendship to all those with faith and also those without it. He listened carefully to what Jane had to say, then admitted that this was a new situation for him and he would have to take some instruction – as he put it – 'back at the ranch'. But, he added, perhaps a prayer? Jane took him to the sluice room, not a part of the hospital usually frequented by gentlemen of the cloth, and showed him the contents of the bucket. He blanched, looked away then knelt down, tacitly inviting Jane to do the same. Taking the cross from around his neck he laid it on the lid of the bucket, held the rim, and prayed that the soul of this unborn child might be received into the Everlasting Kingdom. He then prayed for Dolores Taylor and for 'all those who work in this hospital' that they might have the strength, fortitude and compassion for all that they needed to face. Obviously struggling with his own emotions he then gave a brief nod to Jane and went off – presumably 'back to the ranch'.

At 7am Jane sat down to attempt to put into her night report some sort of coherent account of the night's activities, and this done she was ready to face Sister Bennett and receive her comments. The lady read Jane's efforts in silence. Then, "You've had a rough night, Nurse. Is there anything you want to add?"

"Yes Sister, the baby – the bucket. It's in the sluice, I didn't know what to do with – "

"That's alright, I'll deal with that," the Sister cut in. "Off you go – sleep well."

"Yes Sister, thank you Sister."

Jane scooped up the waiting Nurse Jackson and off they went, until 10pm came around again. And, thought Jane, tonight I will NOT bring my knitting with me. It's obviously a bad omen.

When the pair did return to the ward that evening Jane was surprised to find Sister Bennett still at her desk. "I wanted to talk to you about what happened last night," she said. "What you had to deal with was probably the work of an abortionist. The method of destruction of a viable foetus and the mother's unwillingness to provide us with any information is indicative of ill-practice. I have discussed the whole situation with Mr Corby and he has reported the case to the police. It is now up to them to pursue it or not as they think fit."

Seeing Jane's unhappy face, she added gently, "Abortionists must be stopped, Nurse. They can cause permanent damage and even deaths. We are not seeking to judge or punish the patient, but destroying an unborn child is a criminal offence and the law must be upheld. I, who made the admission, night sister, and the medical staff involved, have all made their statements to the police and I expect that you will be required to do the same."

Jane was discomfited to say the least. Police involvement! Would she have to go to court? Face Dolores across a court room, account for her actions under questioning from a clever barrister?

Sister Bennett was continuing – "I know the ramifications may be less than pleasant. This isn't the first time I have been involved in this sort of situation, but I'm afraid it has to be faced. The lady in question, by the way, took her own discharge this afternoon and has left the premises, very much against our advice of course, but we have no power to retain her." Gathering up her belongings, the sister expressed the hope that Jane would have a quiet night and left to pursue her own affairs.

Jane did make a statement that night to a very personable CID officer, who flirted with her gently and helped her to find the right words. When he left he expressed the hope that they might meet again in pleasanter circumstances. Jane rather hoped so, too. . . What is it about policemen and nurses? Who knows? – but Jane thought that now she knew why Sister Bennett didn't like abortions. She wasn't too keen on them herself!

So, theatre. No one could consider herself trained, competent, complete, capable of enabling any surgical procedure to be undertaken, until she had spent some time being initiated into the business of the operating room. Capable of organising the environment, nursing staff and equipment needed when called upon. The nursing staff were the 'oil' that was an essential component of everything that went on there. 'Oil' that enables the surgeon, the team leader, to practise his craft and eventually to secure a successful outcome.

Two of the group of students working their various ways to their final exam in November 1951 – a date growing ominously closer, had undergone their designated six weeks of theatre training early in the year and had emerged non-committal, glad it was over, and, they said, "interesting, but not for them." This seemed to be a commonly held view, with no one anticipating with any pleasure the day that the monthly duty change went up on the notice board and they saw their name there. Nurse so and so – to theatre.

Why? Wasn't this the drama, the excitement, the 'your life in their hands' scenario of every hospital? A scenario beloved of film makers. Didn't the wide blue eyes of the theatre nurse meet the steady grey ones of the handsome surgeon as he growled out "Scalpel, Nurse." Then later, of course, together they would contemplate with satisfaction and mutual congratulation another life saved.

Not so in reality. The reasons behind this ambiguity towards working in theatre were two-fold. Firstly theatre work was very different from basic nursing. The patient arrived in theatre comatose and covered in green cotton sheets known as theatre towels, with only the bit of him that was to hold the surgeon's interest exposed, and left later, similarly unconscious and covered in blankets. No personality, no communication; the patients as the nurses had come to know them over the last couple of years had vanished. If the art and practice of nursing is roughly divided into three – firstly, comes the doing for a patient those tasks that make him clean and comfortable; tasks that he would do for himself if her were able. Secondly comes the making of observations and the carrying out of treatments, and thirdly the acting as a handmaiden to the medical staff. Theatre work scored highly in the last category. For 'oil' read handmaiden, and if the theatre nurse wasn't handmaidening she was preparing for it, or cleaning up after it. Not a role that appealed to everyone.

The second reason why theatre work was unpopular here at Merton was quite simply the temperament and attitude of the senior sister-in-charge, one Mary Anne. Mary Anne, or to be more formal, Sister M.A. Hornby SRN, SCM, Dip. N (Surgery) had a discontented face set in a permanent mask of bad temper. Her method of training student nurses was to ignore them until they did something that displeased her then bawl them out – and the opportunities for a bawling out were legion. Nervous girls became more nervous, dropping things, spilling things, accidentally 'fouling' things by touching that that was sterile, with that that was not, and generally behaving like the clumsy half-wits she named them. Oh the bliss of Sister Hornby's day off when the whole atmosphere lightened.

All the student nurses had received their theoretical theatre lectures before starting on their placements, so arrived not completely ignorant of their role, but were of course, back to being the most junior individual on the staff complement. The dogsbodies, the 'dirty nurses' as they were known – part of the operating team, but outside the magic circle of those that were gloved, gowned, masked and doing their thing. The dirty nurse was the runner – fetch me, carry me, get me. It was where every theatre nurse started and from where they all aspired to rise to higher things, as indeed they were expected to do over the ensuing six weeks.

When Margery returned from the holiday that followed her three months of night duty, not unexpectedly she found her name on the duty change list pinned to the notice board. N. Harvey to theatre. Anne Mannings name was there also, so there was a bonus, she would have a mate equally as green as herself.

The first thing that struck Margery as she stepped into the theatre suite, was the heat. All theatres, she learned, were super heated to combat the shock that patients suffered when bits of them were exposed to the atmosphere. Just off the theatre proper, through a wide opening, was the sterilising room. Here two large sterilisers were on a rolling boil, and an extractor unit was doing its best – but failing – to remove the steam to the exterior.

167

Whew! Dressed as she was, as were all bodies entering the complex, in turban and mask with a gown over her uniform dress, Margery's mind flew back to the laundry girls, in their particular Turkish bath – not dissimilar. Margery didn't have her hair in curling pins, as they favoured, but frizzy perms were evidently de rigueur for theatre staff, along with damp uniforms and hopefully clear(er) complexions.

History was repeating itself. Everyone flying round with no real time to instruct the newcomers. Half-understood instructions rapped out:

"Get three jugs out of the steriliser, fill them with sterile water and cover the tops with sterile towels and line them up on the side. Seemingly a simple enough instruction. Margery opened the steriliser lid and steam belched forth. Where in this steaming cauldron were the jugs? What did they look like? Big, small, enamel, stainless steel. She couldn't see anything for the hissing, seething water and groped around desperately with cheatle forceps. "Left hand, far corner," – someone instructed – all bodies with hair and face covered look the same. The jugs were heaved out, and filled from a sterile water dispenser, at least that was familiar and Margery carefully draped sterile cotton squares over the jug's mouths. Job done.

Back in the theatre proper, two men and a woman all with bared arms were scrubbing their hands and forearms under running water. A nervous Anne Manning was standing by a row of metal drums. She had been told to go and 'dress the surgeons'. She'd met them before, of course, on the wards, but dressing them was something new. . .

The process was everyday routine for her friend the orthopaedic registrar with whom she had drunk coffee in the small hours of the night, on several occasions, and he helped her out. The first to finish the ten minutes continuous scrubbing that hands had to be subjected to, he whispered, "First a sterile towel – for hands. Now the gown – don't touch it except with forceps – hold it up so I can push my arms in. Now tie the tapes along my back. Gloves? DON'T TOUCH ME. Then with a wink – "later perhaps, at the moment, me sterile, you dirty," and the eyes rolled suggestively. The surgeon and the woman, who Anne found out later, was the junior theatre sister, were discussing Princess Elizabeth's forthcoming foreign tour and whether or not the infant Prince Charles should go too, and took it for granted that when they elbowed the taps to cease the water flow and stood arms held awkwardly away from their bodies, that the right articles would be provided in the right manner to complete their preparations. The conversation continued unabated, Anne ignored. Handmaiden indeed.

The day passed in a blur. Half way through the morning a shout from the sterilising room. Mary Anne was doing her usual round of the two theatres and their adjacent service rooms to ensure that everyone and everything was as it should be. A shout, a bellow "WHO HAS DONE THESE JUGS?"

Margery hurried over. "I did, Sister." What could she possibly have done wrong?

"You do not allow sterile cloths to drape over the outer part of the jug," Mary Anne snapped. "FOULING, Nurse. Are you stupid, have you learnt nothing in school?" and seizing hold of the offending cloths she threw them on the floor and stamped on them, her face contused with scorn and derision and her voice screeching with anger. Margery picked up the offending towels and dropped them in the laundry. The sister had made her point but failed to say how the towels should be arranged satisfactorily. A shout of 'Nurse' from theatre sent her scurrying, so she abandoned the uncovered jugs and she was kept busy fetching and carrying for the next half hour or so. When eventually she returned to the sterilising room, someone had covered two of the jugs with cloths carefully folded into six inch squares. The third jug had gone and was probably in use. Margery had no idea what the jugs of water were for, but now she knew how to cover them adequately. Such a very very small thing in a place where big things happened all the time.

When 1.30pm eventually arrived, Margery and Anne tottered together down to the dining room, shivering slightly in the cooler air of the corridor. Damp, dishevelled and very very thirsty. The first thing that they did was share a jug of water and call for another. Such was to be life in theatre.

When Margery returned at 5pm, after an afternoon off duty, the list of the day's operations was still in progress. The surgeon had retired at lunchtime leaving his registrar to finish the more minor cases and the junior sister had been replaced by a third year student nurse approaching the end of the six week theatre

h

placement. Mary Anne was nowhere to be seen. The poor old houseman was still on his feet assisting the registrar. It was nine hours since the first patient of the day had been wheeled in. Margery hoped that someone had allowed him a lunch break. What a difference in the atmosphere now. The anaesthetist had light music playing on a portable radio and the registrar was discussing with his assistant the previous week's football results.

By 6.30pm the day's undertakings were complete. Two fingers amputated, two broken hips repaired, one bone graft, two meniscectomies (removal of knee cartilages) and three lots of bunions removed. A good day's work. Had the 'new' student nurses found any satisfaction therein? Well, they had to remember that their small contributions added to the whole. Get the little things right and prevent bigger things going wrong. Wasn't there a saying by someone, somewhere that began, "For want of a nail. . ." Or was it something to do with a butterfly's wing that Margery was thinking of? She couldn't remember, and anyway it wasn't important. She just had to be sure to always have a nail ready when it was wanted!

When, as a junior, Margery had spent a portion of each night cleaning, in one or other of the two theatres, she had thought that was it all. A sensible use of junior labour to save those capable of higher things to be free to perform more sophisticated tasks during the day. Quite untrue, she now realised. With the completion of the list a frenzy of cleaning began. "One does not clean because articles are dirty. One cleans to prevent them getting so," she was told. Sterilisers emptied, cleaned, re-filled. Instruments cleaned and counted yet again. Dressing drums re-packed and sent for autoclaving. The doctors' changing room tidied, discarded masks, caps and gowns picked up and sent to the laundry; white wellingtons paired up and ash trays emptied. By 7pm they were finished, so then the preparations for tomorrow began. The never-ending round.

Of course, there were moments of high drama in theatre. A laparotomy (exploratory surgery; 'an open him up and see what we can see' exercise) might reveal something unexpected. Hearts can suddenly stop beating; bleeding prove uncontrollable. Nothing is certain. The human form comes with many variations and patients' reaction to what, after all, is an unnatural intervention can be unexpected. Always in a rush and the opportunities for human error are manifold. On the whole, however, Anne was vaguely surprised at the routine smoothness with which a day's work was accomplished. Mary Anne presided over the trolley of instruments for most mornings, expertly and accurately slapping into the surgeon's hand, handle first, whatever she anticipated he needed. She saved her invective for the nursing staff, continuing to issue orders and instructions, with impatience for inefficiency and what she perceived as ineptitude, from her 'scrubbed' position alongside the operating table. A new houseman might be indiscreet enough to stretch out his hand towards 'her' instruments on 'her' trolley. He only did it once. A sharp smack over the knuckles with a pair of Spencer-Wells artery forceps, told him wordlessly to mind his own business, and she would mind hers.

How expressive are eyes Anne thought. She was hovering on the periphery of the business in hand, ready and willing to fetch and carry. The girls with turbans pulled low over their foreheads, the men with their round theatre caps similarly pulled down, and both with surgical masks covering the lower half of their faces, it was only by their eyes that they could be recognised. Eyes that spoke volumes. Concentration, amusement, annoyance, sometimes with a hint of panic. They held enquiry, delivered instruction, asked questions and sometimes rolled, winked or flirted blatantly.

Anne was brought out of her reverie by the voice of the anaesthetist. "Two down, nine letters, Stealthily Machiavellian," he announced. He was doing the crossword in *The Daily Mail,* the newspaper propped up on the diathermy machine. Once a patient has reached the required level of anaesthesia, though his general condition is continually under the eye of the 'gas man', it takes only routine effort to maintain the status quo, and diversions via the daily news sheets were not uncommon.

The surgeon's hands were in the patient's abdomen, he was removing that part of his stomach that had developed an ulcer. A not uncommon operation but one designated as 'major' on the league table.

"Deceitful," he suggested. "Is that nine letters? Does it have two l's?"

"Not sure."

Anne just couldn't resist it. She'd had a look at the paper in her lunch break. "It's insidious," she announced – a voice from outer space. The surgeon turned round and his eyes grinned. The anaesthetist waggled his pencil at her in salute.

"Thank you, Nurse." And Mary Anne? Her eyes were shooting arrows of fire in Anne's direction. Ah well, Anne thought, I can only die once and at least I now know that a reasonable vocabulary helps in this handmaidening lark.

Week two, nearly into week three, Margery was to be trusted with the job of 'doing mops', a step forward from theatre running. 'Doing mops' meant that she was to be in charge of the counting out of mops, or swabs, needed for each operation, and ensuring that the same number was returned. Stories of swabs or even instruments lost in a patient's abdomen were well known. That this had happened somewhere, sometime was probably true, but Margery, feeling the frisson of her responsibility keenly, was quite determined that it wouldn't happen here, and certainly not now.

Large theatre swabs, perhaps six or eight inches square and of many thicknesses of gauze and each with a substantial loop of tape at the corner, are difficult to lose, but a two inch square of folded gauze, screwed up and blood soaked lurking in a corner? A different story. Margery had a board full of numbered hooks on which to account for the taped swabs – a bit like a quoits board, – and a mackintosh sheet spread to receive small swabs from the bundles of six that had been so laboriously cut and assembled by the ward staff in the small hours of the morning.

Used swabs were tossed out by surgeon or assistant in the general direction of where Margery stood, two or three feet to the rear, and these she retrieved lining them up in sixes, or hooking them onto her board. When she heard the phrase, "Ready to close. Mops' Nurse?" She could reply:

"All correct sir." Wow! An important job in anyone's imagination, even if the principal skill needed was the ability to count.

Margery had been warned to watch out for a certain general surgeon. He had a habit, when he saw that a newcomer had been entrusted with the mops, of hiding a small swab under his size 12 theatre boot, then watching a panic stricken mops' nurse counting and re-counting, unable to match the 'ins' with the 'outs'. Now, if he played that trick she could reply to his question, "All correct, Nurse?" with, "Yes, sir, if I include the one under your left heel." Not a popular man.

The theatre porter was a small weasel of a man, known to everyone as Herbert. Herbert maintained this favoured position by virtue of his long service. He'd been pushing trolleys now for thirty years and had reached the climax of his career in his present occupation which was a relatively light one. No humping of unpleasant dirty dressing bins, no heaving of heavy wet linen, no being at the beck and call of the whole hospital, he was responsible only to the theatre staff, and his duties were principally wheeling patients to and from theatre and doing anything else that required a bit of muscle. This left him plenty of time to sit in a corner of the sterilising room with the *Racing Post*, ready to fulfil any task required, but meanwhile marking the paper with his fancies for Kempton Park and the like.

Recently an establishment calling itself a 'Turf Accountant' had opened in an empty shop near to the hospital and Herbert had found himself a nice little earner advising the medical staff as to where to place their money, taking it down to the bookies and returning with the winnings, if any. He then received an 'appreciation' pro rata, and everyone was happy. Herbert got the excitement of betting with someone else's cash, and the medical fraternity were saved the indignity of hanging around in a betting shop. A symbiotic arrangement.

Anne hated amputations. Some of the orthopaedic instruments were reminiscent of those hanging on the wall of her dad's shed, and the sound of bone being sawn through she felt in the soles of her feet. Therefore, to have a severed limb, albeit shrouded in theatre towels, placed in your arms, she was the runner that morning, was not conducive to her equilibrium. Muttering words no nice lady should use, she dumped the offending leg in the sink and regarded it tentatively. It still had a pair of artery forceps dangling from it, for goodness sake, and there were towel clips holding the bundle together. What was she supposed to do with it? Seeing her dilemma, Herbert put down his newspaper and intervened. "Give it here," he said, "before the bugger walks off of its own accord." And seizing the blood stained bundle he committed the heinous crime of opening the outer door of the sterilising room, a door intended as a fire exit, and which everyone knew must not be opened unnecessarily whilst the theatre was in use.

Herbert trotted off down the path outside, Anne in hot pursuit.

If he put the leg into the hospital furnace as she feared was his intention and it was needed for laboratory tests, dissection or forensic investigation and she had allowed it. What then? She caught him up, relieved him of the leg, came back in, closed the fire door and peered into the theatre. Everything was continuing as normal no one aware of the black comedy being enacted nearby.

The leg was back on the draining board. Anne removed the bits of metal attached to it – they would be needed for the final count of instruments, put the towels in the laundry and the leg went into a bucket. It was at this point that hysterical laughter seized her. She coughed and spluttered and shook with nervous half-suppressed giggles. Tears rolled down her face. She gulped and gasped and finally, tension broken, her humourless laughter subsided and reality returned.

As she was dropping off to sleep that night, it occurred to Anne to wonder? When a patient signed the routine consent form prior to surgery, she had always understood that it was just giving permission for a general anaesthetic to be administered. Did it also confer the right to somebody to dispose of any bits and pieces as they thought fit? She would re-read the familiar consent form in the morning. That is, if she could be bothered.

The question niggled. The bits and pieces, in today's case, a leg, was surely the property of the patient and he should have a say in what happened to it. Perhaps pickled in formalin for future students to peer at. Perhaps used by medical students for dissection. Perhaps just burnt. Did such items have a monetary value? She'd heard of itinerants selling the odd pint or two of their blood. Wasn't it in America? Was it possible to sell a leg? To medical schools. More black humour threatened. Advertise perhaps in *Exchange and Mart* 'One foreleg (male, forty years). Whole apart from some necrosis to toes. Deep frozen. Offers please from registered medical schools only.'

Anne turned over and wriggled herself into a more comfortable position. Such complicated medico-legal-ethical-moral problems she would leave for others to ponder. Her days were quite full enough.

Margery and Anne completed their six weeks in theatre. They weathered scrubbing up with Mary Anne for several cases. The hissed instructions, the derisory glares, the expectations of

174

ineptitude causing them, as it had others, to drop and muddle things and render their minds void and their brains to cease functioning. The teaching process as carried out by that certain person in charge. They each managed several cases independently and successfully before they thankfully returned to 'proper nursing'.

The incessant repetitive cleaning, the moments of high tension, of extreme temperaments, the routine of routine surgery, they left behind. It had been an experience.

Chapter Thirteen

It was said, and widely believed, that if an individual sat in the reception hall of the outpatients department at Merton Royal Infirmary for a six month period of time, then he or she would see, during their sojourn there, the whole of the population of Merton town pass through for one reason or another. Unlikely, but possible, and certainly unproven!

Of course, anybody and everybody could, if they so wished, enter the hospital grounds through the main gates, traverse the drive and enter the building through the pillared portico and main door; make their way down the main admin. corridor (admiring the marble busts of illustrious founders on the way) and eventually reach the ward or department that they sought. In practice only the few who owned a car and needed parking space used the main door, the majority preferring the outpatients' entrance which gave access to a street of terraced houses, small shops and the convenience of the local bus stop. Thus the main aisle through the centre of the Outpatients' Department waiting hall was a constant stream of people. Staff, volunteers, delivery men, outside service providers, patients and their accompanying relatives and, of course, their visitors.

As the visiting hours for the wards were limited to one hour on each of two afternoons, and half an hour on each of two evenings, with only two visitors allowed at each bedside, these periods were anticipated eagerly by all concerned. The reception hall would begin to fill up with anxious eager relatives well before the appointed hour. Two porters were stationed at the end of the aisle leading to the wards and there they would stand like two Horatios' holding back the masses, until at two minutes before the appointed hour, when they stood back – and the hall emptied like a bottle with its stopper removed.

The hall itself was filled with rows of hard wooden benches, securely bolted to the floor. Countless bottoms over the years had polished these seats to smoothness, as patients sat, squirmed and slid along the benches as they worked their way through to the front row and the ultimate source of treatment and advice that they were seeking.

To the left, off the hall, were the consulting rooms used for the many outpatients' clinics, and to the right were the entrances to the X-ray department, Physiotherapy and the Pharmacy. At the far end was the Accident and Emergency department. A totally inadequate facility for the hundreds of patients it sought to serve. Two cubicles, each with a bed, a small theatre for minor operations, and two dressing stations. With no permanent medical staff, the two housemen on casualty duty sat either end of a small table, each with a chair for a patient. They heard the story, eyed the source of trouble and passed them on, as necessary, to whatever their complaint might warrant, referral to X-ray, stitching, bandaging, injection or admission.

Cutting across this hive of activity were hold-ups caused by patients arriving by ambulance. In the case of those sent in by GP's for emergency treatment impossible to undertake at home, there was usually some warning, but for the accidents arriving straight, as it were, from the roadside, there was no such luxury and anything might arrive at the door, from the dead, the badly injured and nearly dead, to those with minor accidents sustained in the home. Ambulance personnel were trained in basic first aid and were competent in immobilising possible fractures and arresting haemorrhage, but were employed as much for their driving skills and ability to lift awkward heavy weights as for their medical knowledge. "Scoop 'em up and drive like hell to the nearest hospital," was the principle self-admitted function of the ambulance service. If these accidents occurred at a time when the hall was choc-a-bloc with visitors waiting to see their loved ones, the ambulance staff forged their way through the throng by the simple expedient of yelling. Meanwhile the rows of the lame, those in pain and the blind waited on their wooden benches. And waited. And waited.

It was into this maelstrom of activity that Audrey Renton and Margaret Woods arrived in the summer of 1951. Finals were looming and lectures had increased to two and sometimes three per week. Both the girls were looking forward to their time in 'Cas'. It was exciting, it was varied, and their interaction with patients was intense but transient. Not for those nurses relishing quiet vigilance nor for those who enjoyed routine caring with the reward of witnessing progressive recovery. But what ho! For anyone purporting to be interested in their fellow humans, their reactions, values and adventures in everyday living, it provided endless material. Many and varied were the difficulties people inflicted upon themselves at home. Beads and other small objects were pushed into ears and noses; chip pans caught fire resulting in singed hair and burnt fingers, razor blades slipped and mats were fallen over; noxious liquids accidentally and sometimes deliberately drunk. Then there were the industrial accidents. Welding sparks burnt eyes, ends of fingers were chopped off, chisels wrongly used, chiselled palms and heavy weights were dropped on unprotected feet. All these were regarded as minor injuries and were, after medical perusal, largely dealt with by the nursing staff in the persons of Margaret and Audrey under the watchful eye of a staff nurse. 'New girls' in this environment they had not yet learnt to suture (stitch) – a skill not on the curriculum but one taught 'on the job' and an added extra to a competent nurse's repertoire.

Audrey dosed an eight year old with ipecacuana and sat her in a corner with a vomit bowl under the watchful eye of her mum. She had eaten some laburnum seeds, those lovely little pea pods just right for a dolly's picnic. . .

Bandaging skills learnt long ago in PTS came into play, Vaseline gauze was applied to burns, aspirins doled out and ribs strapped with elastoplast. One such patient, a hefty young man with cracked ribs, was saved from future discomfort in the nick of time by the staff nurse. "Shave his chest first, before you apply yards of sticking plaster," she snapped. "You're applying support – not a depletory." Of course. Margaret would remember in future.

Busy dressing yet another contusion, Audrey caught, couldn't avoid, hearing a tale of woe recounted to the duty doctor by a worried mother. It concerned her daughter who, she said, "had swallowed Princess Margaret Rose." As the said princess had recently attained her majority, and with the birth of Prince Charles, a recent event, interest in the Royal family was at a high. Small memorabilia were being sold in the shops and this particular model had it seemed ended up in an unintended and unusual location. The doctor showed neither alarm or surprise at this unusual announcement.

"And how big is the Princess?" he enquired.

The woman indicated about an inch.

"And would she be made of tin perhaps? Or wood? Or plastic?"

The mother thought plastic.

"Good", said the doctor. "In that case the nurse here will give you a bottle of Californian syrup of figs. I want you to give your daughter a spoonful at bedtime for the next three nights. And may I take this opportunity to wish Her Royal Highness Many Happy Returns? The young man waited for the woman to leave, clutching her daughter in one hand and the bottle of laxative in the other, before letting out a roar of laughter which turned into a snort. Then sobering quickly he turned to his next patient.

An amusing incident, overhead not just by Audrey, but probably by everyone else in the department including the five patients brought in from the benches outside and waiting their imminent consultation. The cramped conditions allowed for no confidentiality whatsoever. In fact the concept of that, and of the preserving of patients' right of privacy and dignity came low down on all the staffs' pre-occupations. They were there to heal the body presented, with what was available to them, in a given time scale and in an environment which left much to be desired. Embarrassment and reticence had to be endured, niceties that were desirable but under the circumstances often forgotten or impossible.

Where, however, the concept of confidentiality between health professionals and their patients was being promoted was in the erstwhile taboo subject of sexually transmitted diseases. Men had returned home after long periods away from their families; periods spent in places where sex was cheap and available. Many brought back home something more than they had taken with them. The myth that – 'you can get the clap from a camel, you know' persisted. In an attempt to open up the subject, contain the disease, encourage sufferers to seek treatment for, in the main, their very curable afflictions, a publicity campaign had been launched by The Ministry of Health. Films were shown in cinemas, talks broadcast on the radio, and posters appeared in public places.

These efforts spawned the usual crop of dissenters using the local press. "No respectable person should be forced to see/hear of such disgusting subjects."

"Innocent children, wives and mothers should be spared the knowledge of these sordid diseases," etc, etc. 'Disgusted of every town' was in full flow.

What the poster and so on were assuring, was the complete confidentiality that would be maintained concerning the identity of individuals attending the VD clinics and the simplicity of treatment. There followed the possibility of long term horrors if symptoms were ignored; then the dates, times and places where help were offered.

Merton Royal Infirmary's response was to set up two evening clinics (one for men, one for women) in the main outpatient hall. To this end large rigid wooden screens were wheeled in to isolate the required number of benches from the public eye. Treatment cards were printed that recorded only an identification number – no names were used. This service was to be staffed by one consultant and the senior outpatient sister only, each of whom, supposedly, could be relied upon to be both deaf and blind if the need arose. All very worthy efforts. Perhaps one might think it *un*worthy to add that a large notice was hung on the first screen, which stated – VD CLINIC THIS WAY → and that treatment cards were printed on bright red card and bore the title VD CLINIC. In the field of confidentiality there was still a lot to learn.

On her second day in casualty, when Margaret was ushering a further five individuals into the department proper, her eyes swept over the benches and their occupants in the hall. For a moment she thought that she saw her grandmother sitting amongst the assembly, then realised she was wrong – she was seeing just another grey haired elderly lady with glasses and a comfortable bosom. Not giving her another thought, the day's work engulfed her in the usual manner. The following day the lady was there again, sitting almost at the back, and the following week there she was once more. Funny, this lady never seemed to reach the front and be seen and treated, unless of course she always arrived there when Margaret was at lunch. She would investigate.

When patients arrived in the casualty department they registered their presence with a clerk who sat in a glass lean-to office surrounded by banks of files. Everyone in the hospital knew Mavis – as did half of Merton. She had occupied her glass box for many, many years and there was nothing Mavis didn't know about the outpatients' department. Truculent youths, somewhat the worse for a mid-day drink, quietened under her stern gaze, and unruly children quailed as their mothers warned, "That lady is watching you." If conversation between patients became too obtrusive, Mavis's terse comments of "This is a hospital not a bar-parlour; can we keep the noise down, please," was met with a lessening of chat. She knew the regulars, identified the lost, the frightened and the plain obnoxious, so of course it was to Mavis that Margaret brought the query about the old lady.

"Ah," said Mavis, "that will be Emily. She comes about twice a week. She likes someone to chat to and enjoys hearing about other people's problems. There's always some activity to watch here – and company. Besides it saves on her heating bills and she can get a cup of tea at the WVS snack bar."

Margaret was intrigued. "What happens when she gets to the doctor?"

"Oh she never does," was the reply. "When she gets to the end of the second row she moves backwards and starts again." Problem solved.

Margaret and Audrey both learned to suture, and to calculate the amount of local anaesthetic necessary, in the coming week. Out came an orange again, as in those far off days when they learnt how to give an injection, and they both practised sewing together gaping slashes in the rind with neat nylon stitches. Another skill to be exercised in the many opportunities that the days presented.

"You'll never guess what came in today?" Audrey's eyes were popping with anticipation of the telling.

181

"No, I don't suppose we will," said Jane who had done her stint in Casualty. "Anything can happen and usually does in that department."

They were all tired. The strain of extra lectures, and full days of work and now the extra responsibilities that their status as a third year student had earned them, were taking their toll.

"Well come on, you're obviously dying to tell." – Eileen was embroidering forget-me-nots onto a British Home Stores nightie to make it more trousseau-worthy.

"Well," Began Audrey, "what came in, was a gentleman who had got his wife's wedding ring stuck on that part of his anatomy usually kept in his trousers."

A quickening of interest – this might be worth hearing.

"What did they do?" Eileen asked, "send for the fire brigade and a hacksaw?"

"Ouch! No. It was Dr Preston from Morris Ward on duty. First he plastered it with Vaseline and tried to, sort of, screw it off!!"

"I hope," said Eileen, "you use the word 'screw' in the literal sense!"

Audrey ignored her, she was enjoying herself. "That didn't work so he sent down to the kitchen for a bowl of ice and he (that is the patient – not Dr Preston) knelt over it and dipped himself in." By now everyone was chortling. "The ring came off, and the chap just pocketed it, heaved up his trousers and said – 'Thank you, Doctor, I'll see she doesn't do that again' – and vanished. What aplomb!" Life in casualty was never dull.

Dr Akumbo, the gentleman of colour whose arrival some months ago had caused such surprise and curiosity amongst the staff, was now an established part of the work force. Liked, respected, integrated – that is amongst his co-workers. One or two individuals had made a play for his attentions. These he had been heard to dismiss as, "Nice girls trying to be naughty girls with the big black man," and to in-patients his acceptance by staff and others soon broke down any discomfort they may have felt at the presence of this alien in their midst.

Margaret and Audrey had now been in Casualty for eight weeks and were such old hands that they were both trusted with the 1.30pm to 10pm shift from time to time, and during the period 8pm to 10pm left alone and in sole charge to deal with whatever walked through the door. A doctor was 'on call' somewhere in the building, as was the night sister, but fingers crossed they wouldn't be needed for these were usually the quietest hours of the day. Clinics, daily treatment rooms, minor ops, were over for the day. Small domestic accidents were often left by the victims or their parents to deal with in the morning. Night life, with all that that could throw up had hardly begun. Time Margaret decided to tidy up generally, mop the floor, empty bins, boil up the steriliser yet again and straighten the furniture.

Not to be. Appearing at the door were two policemen. Between them, her scalp covered in blood, was a woman wailing noisily. One policeman had in his hand what Margaret took to be a small furry animal. As they came close she realised, with a sickening jolt that what it was, was hair. Ye Gods, had this woman been scalped? But the policemen were grinning at her discomfiture and Margaret felt a wave of irritation at their attitude. They sat the woman down and Margaret saw that 'she' had several days' growth of beard on 'her' chin, and that 'her' hands, now clutching 'her' head were large and masculine.

The policeman jiggled what Margaret now realised was a wig in front of the patient, who grabbed it and stuffed it in his pocket. "Got thrown head first into a bramble patch," it was explained. "Nothing serious. We got there before the lads really got going. They don't like queers on their patch," it was explained.

The scalped woman was a badly scratched man with an identity problem. Margaret washed his head, sprayed on some antiseptic and made him quite a fetching turban from a triangular bandage intended for a sling. No need to send for medical help.

Dr Akumbo had been accepted to play for Merton's men's hockey team, and was attempting to get fit before the season started by going for a run each evening. Track-suited and somewhat sweaty he stuffed his stethoscope into his trouser pocket and decided he would look in on casualty. "Anything doing?" Margaret told him of the scalped woman who had turned out to be a scratched man and they shared the joke of her misunderstanding before he went off to the doctors' quarters. 9.30pm, half an hour to go, and all was quiet.

Until. . . Dr Akumbo had scarcely left the department when three young men stumbled in. One had a wound of some sort over his eye which had bled profusely, his face bedaubed and his tee-shirt red and sticky. The other two were his mates, there to support him, and all three were high on booze and the euphoria of a recent fracas at which they had claimed victory. Not exactly drunk but each with the bravado, the leering conviction that they were God's gift to all things female. They eyed Margaret appreciatively.

"Hallo darling. Our mate needs his eye seeing to."

"Oh, oh, I'm coming over faint myself. Help me, Nursie."

This accompanied by much staggering around and head clutching. The first one eyed her, then attempted to slide an arm round her waist. Margaret was surprised to find that she didn't feel frightened – alone as she was – but angry, irritated and with an overwhelming urge to swat them out of existence. She couldn't of course, so she did the next best thing and with a sharp "STOP THAT!" jabbed him in the stomach with her elbow.

"Ho, ho, a feisty one, I like a fighter," and the arm round her waist tightened, so she trod down hard on his instep. This set him hopping in supposed agony whilst his mates, propped on a bench, roared with laughter.

"GET OUT!" the authoritative male voice silenced them for a moment. Dr Akumbo had nipped into the 'gents' on his way back to his room and had heard the noise as he emerged and returned. The trio recovered.

"Bloody Hell – a black man!"

"What are you doing here, Darkie?"

Dr Akumbo was a large man and fit. When the three showed no inclination to move he took a collar in each hand and frog marched the two supporting mates out into the hall, releasing them both with a non-too-gentle push.

Back inside, the injured man, now without his supporters had slid down into the corner. The doctor approached him with a view to examining his injury. "Don't you come near me," he yelled, "with your dirty black hands."

The doctor sighed. "It looks like it only needs one stitch Nurse, will you do it, or shall I?"

The patient's eyes slid between the man who he now realised was a doctor and the nurse who looked to him to be hardly old enough to have left school.

"I'll do it," said Margaret anticipating that the alternative might result in more abuse, and indicated the minor ops theatre.

184

Lying on the table the patient began to sing tunelessly to himself and Margaret cleaned up his face. It was when she was threading the needle that she felt a touch, a grope along her thigh. Another spurt of anger hit Margaret, she could hardly stitch his face unless she came close. Winding the table down to a lower level, she knelt forcibly on the wandering hand and looked hard at him from above. "I have in my hand," she said, "a curved and extremely sharp needle. If you do not lie absolutely still, I may *accidentally* get it embedded in your eyeball. DO YOU UNDERSTAND?" The patient remained motionless.

Meanwhile, in the waiting hall, the other two were running along the benches, leaping between the rows. When Dr Akumbo emerged uttering the word "OUT," they invited:

"Come and join us, monkey man, you should be good at this." But 16 stones of angry black man, looking as if he wanted to tear them limb from limb, proved too much. They went, followed by their subdued friend now sporting a large sticking plaster. It was now ten minutes to ten. The whole episode had taken just 20 minutes.

"I'm sorry," Margaret felt it was somehow necessary to apologise to Dr Akumbo.

"Sorry! What for exactly?"

"Well, I'm ashamed of what they said to you and I'm white like them and you're not, and well. . ." Margaret ground to a halt, not quite sure what she was trying to say.

"For goodness sake, Nurse, on those sort of grounds perhaps I should apologise to you – on behalf of the male sex in general! So let's face it, you and I are part of an oppressed minority." He shrugged, "C'est la vie. We should be thankful that our professions and status give us the self-possession to rise above it. Others haven't that privilege. I really must get changed. Do I pong?"

"Yes," said Margaret with a grin, "you do a bit."

When the night staff arrived in the next few minutes, all was quiet, the department empty.

"Anything out of the ordinary to report?" the staff nurse, who was facing the next 10 hours on duty slung her cape onto a chair.

"No," Margaret said, "not really."

It was interesting to note however, that in the next few days a panic button was installed. For the use of those working alone at night.

It was getting ever nearer. Four weeks, then three – two, one. Finals loomed. Everyone was getting tetchy. There were those that shrugged and feigned, not confidence exactly, but an indifference based on 'whatever will be will be'. Those that carried lists around with them – lists of drug dosages, incubation periods, acceptable readings for various diagnostic tests, trying in odd moments to memorise such things. Then there were those that clung to lucky mascots that they didn't really believe in, but which didn't do any harm and might just help to make the difference. After all, footballers had their lucky pieces of kit didn't they? So why shouldn't a lucky sixpence be slipped into a shoe or a beloved teddy bear sitting on the desk be helpful?

The written exams were to be taken in the classroom of course, as were the practicals. The four training schools, situated within a reasonable radius of Merton, took it in turns to host both the exams and the outside examiners who were sent down by the General Nursing Council to officiate. At least the Merton girls would not be in an alien hospital this year, but in familiar surroundings, which must be a help.

Tradition, tradition. The day before the commencement of the exams it was the usual practice for candidates to be entertained to afternoon tea by Matron in her flat. The first and last time they had the opportunity to enter this private space that her status had earned her, and something of an occasion to be endured as the precursor of the coming final exams.

Perhaps it was the fact that Matron was out of uniform and at her most charming self that helped the girls to relax, for in spite of the presence of Miss Bailey-Scott, relax they did, and stuffed themselves with dainty sandwiches and more robust sausage rolls. Then came – THE CAKE. Especially made for the occasion by the kitchen staff, it had the hospital crest drawn in icing sugar on the top, and six horseshoes round the sides, one for each of them.

They all had a slice and pronounced it excellent, and then it was time for Matron's speech. She told them that she had every faith in them and their ability to succeed. Then she paid tribute to Miss Bailey-Scott who had guided, taught and mentored them over the last three years. The girls weren't too sure about this, but beamed and clapped as was expected, and with a final instruction to get a good night's sleep, they dispersed.

It was odd, the following day, to find the sitting room full of strange coloured uniforms, as the finalists from surrounding schools gathered.

"Fancy having to wear pink dresses," Eileen whispered to Margaret as they waited for the invigilator to call them into the school.

"Better than the purple ones," she answered, "they're from Blackpool. Trust Blackpool to dress its nurses in something loud and flashy."

"You," Eileen replied, "are being rude about my revered home town, so shut up."

They giggled but decided that their own navy and white stripes were definitely superior. Then they soberly filed into the examination room.

What can one say of a written exam. Three papers. One on medical and one on surgical nursing. Then there was general nursing, which Anne said, was to cover the bits they'd not been able to fit in the other two. It was much as expected, some things they were unfamiliar with, much much more than they had been taught and practised, and practised, again. One pink uniform walked out in tears after half an hour. A lot of pen chewing and a lot of frantic writing. They did their best and time would tell.

And so to the practical exam. Miss Bailey-Scott had explained that the content here would depend entirely on the whim of the examiner. Nurses may be asked to talk through a nursing procedure and gather together the appropriate equipment. They may be asked to 'set up' a specific tray or trolley for someone else to use (ie a doctor), or assemble all the instruments and necessities for a specific surgical operation. Or just talk – and answer – as required. There was obviously little hope of assembling real people willing to swallow stomach tubes, have needles stuck into their backsides, or their bodies repeatedly handled, bathed or treated just to satisfy examiners that a procession of student nurses had benefited adequately from their training.

If the truth were known Miss Bailey-Scott was uneasy herself about this invasion of her territory by these examiners sent down by the revered General Nursing Council. At the top of their professions, would they look down their superior noses at her and her small northern hospital; find the equipment it provided for training and examining the students inadequate? She wouldn't admit even to herself that she was harbouring such thoughts. After all, she had trained at what was considered to be one of the best schools in the world: St Thomas' – Miss Nightingales own foundation, and she was conveying their standards to the next generation. She adjusted her cap, straightened her back and sallied forth to play the charming host to these powerful strangers from the south.

Audrey Renton and Eileen Downey were called into the familiar practical room together and each allocated to an examiner. They were sitting at either end of the large room, surrounded it seemed by all the equipment the training room could muster.

Audrey, if not exactly bursting with confidence, felt that she had worked diligently and systematically through three years of notes and could have done no more.

The lady, not in uniform, smiled and bade her sit down and launched into the business to hand. "If, Nurse, you looked at me, as you just did, and had seen that the whites of my eyes were yellow, and my skin had a yellowish tinge, what would you think was wrong?"

This was easy, and Audrey opened her mouth to state the obvious, "You've got jaundice," – the vernacular reaction of anyone, nurse or lay person to such a question. She stopped herself in time. One didn't 'get' jaundice like one 'got' measles, head lice, or arthritic joints. Jaundice was a symptom not a disease, so she adjusted her answer to, "I'd think your skin and eyes were jaundiced."

"Yes, why?"

"Bile salts in your blood are staining your skin."

"Why?"

"Possibly you have a blocked bile duct and bile can't enter the duodenum and so it is absorbed by capillaries."

"Why would it block?"

"Calculi, infection, new growth."

The examiner smiled. "Ah yes – one can always safely throw in 'new growth' to most answers. Any other reason for the jaundice?"

"Liver malfunction, infective hepatitis, cirrhosis, n. . ." Audrey started to say 'new growth' and changed it to "carcinoma." Please God, she prayed, don't let her get on to the haemolytics – I'm not too sure about those.

"Thank you, Nurse, then of course there are the haemolytic jaundices – but enough of me and my complexion."

Thank goodness, prayer answered. Out of the corner of her eye Audrey could see Eileen assembling cervical dilators she was evidently preparing for a D and C.

The examiner was continuing. "When a patient is admitted to a ward for whatever reason, it is usual to do a routine urine test. Use the tray on the side there and bring me the result of any test you would do."

Audrey had done such tests many times. She lit the spirit lamp provided and considered. First, one would take the specific gravity. She knew how to do this and how to record her findings, but its significance escaped her, so she decided to skip that in case it led to awkward questions. Now sugar. She carefully measured an inch of Benedicts solution into a test tube and added eight drops of urine and heated it pointing the test tube away from herself. A small amount of liquid in a test tube boils quickly – a sudden squirt in the eye made one careful. It looked as if this particular wee-wee contained sugar, the liquid was turning green then orange. If there was sugar, there might also be ketones – so she tested for that and for bile, blood and pus – nothing.

In view of the sugar present, there followed a discussion on diabetes and the control of carbohydrate intake and the giving of the right amount of insulin. Could Nurse perhaps describe the different symptoms of an insulin coma and one where hyperglycaemia was the cause? Nurse could and did.

Eileen, meanwhile having disposed of the collecting together of gynaecological instruments, was demonstrating how to bind a new born child onto an x-shaped wooden splint prior to surgery for a pyloric stenosis. Then she too was dismissed with a "Thank you, Nurse, you may go!"

Of course there was a post mortem that evening, no exam could be undertaken without one. Three years of lectures and ward and department experience condensed into a few hours, cherry picking from a sea of information; on which to base the success or failure and therefore the future careers of those examined. It was ever so. "What I want to know," said Anne that evening. "Is where did they get the urine that several of us tested during the exam?"

"The Scaley-Bott of course," said Jane. "She provided all the other equipment."

"Nah, she wouldn't. Besides it had sugar in it."

"Perhaps she's a closet diabetic."

"More likely she 'fed' it with a spoonful of her sugar ration, or perhaps she ordered Clarry to do the whole lot." Anne's imagination was on overtime. "I can just picture it," she said, imitating the two voices, " 'Clarry, Clarry.' 'Coming Miss Bailey-Scott.' 'Urine, please Clarry' – and off she scuttled. What a good thing we didn't spill it or the Scaley-Bott would have had to stop proceedings whilst Clarry ran off to the toilet with a jar."

This ridiculous scenario had them all laughing in an orgy of post-stress hysteria. It was over.

They didn't have long to wait for the results, perhaps two weeks or so. They had been given no specific date or time, but as the days passed every nerve was braced. They knew how it would be, they'd heard it in the past. Matron's voice would come over the Tannoy system that reached every part of the building. "This is Matron. Would all state finalists report to my office please. All state finalists please." Hurrying down, people called out 'good luck' as they passed, the whole hospital would soon know of their success or failure.

They passed. All of them. Matron stood with a handful of blue belts to distribute, Miss Bailey-Scott beaming at her side. The girls felt as if their waists were illuminated with fairy lights as they made their way back to the wards. Now people were calling out 'congratulations' and patting backs, shaking hands. They were State Registered Nurses.

As Margery approached the door of Lister Ward on her way back to her own work place, she was stopped by the ward sister, who was obviously on the look-out for her return from Matron's office. "Congratulations, Nurse Harvey," she said, "are you on duty this afternoon?"

"Yes?"

"Good. My staff nurse is on her day off and I find I have an urgent errand in town. Will you be on call for my ward?"

Yesterday Margery had been left in charge of the ward where

she was currently working, but with an invisible life line to a senior nurse to use if needed. Today she would be similarly in charge, but with no life line. In addition she was being asked to be just that for the staff of another ward. A ward she knew, where she had worked in the past, but with 20 or so patients that were unknown to her. "Yes Sister, of course," she replied. After all, she was a staff nurse now. A new life was beginning.

Chapter Fourteen

A beginning and an ending. Goodbye to the nurse training school. To Miss Bailey-Scott, to Clarry, to Mrs Green and Jimmy. Hello to more responsibility and to the consideration of fresh horizons.

Margaret Woods worked for six months as a staff nurse and completed the year, as the rules allowed, by transferring to the school of midwifery adjacent to the main hospital. She completed her midwifery training just as her fiancé was offered his first parish and appointment as vicar. They never did travel to the foreign mission field, deciding that God's word was needed just as much at home as it was needed abroad. They married and Margaret became the chatelaine of a large and very draughty Victorian parsonage. She ran the Mother's Union, taught Sunday School, and acted as an unpaid district nurse to the elderly of the parish and as mentor and friend to young mothers and their broods. Life was very full.

Jane Kirby worked her twelve months as a staff nurse, then followed her inclination to work with children. She was accepted by Great Ormond St Children's Hospital to undertake a shortened course there, and became a Registered Sick Children's Nurse. A famous hospital and life in the capital city. She couldn't wait!

Anne Manning 'staffed' for the required twelve months then surprisingly took a job on a whim that she had seen advertised in a national newspaper. She became the matron of a boy's public school. The junior department, 30 small boys aged 8 to 12 years.

Here she not only enlivened the days of her small charges, but started the pulses racing of several academics in the staff room. Individuals whose sexual muscles had long been dormant.

Audrey Renton just disappeared. She did her twelve months as a staff nurse then one day moved on. A woman to whom communal life meant very little, and whose private life remained private. No one heard from her again.

Eileen Downey defied Matron and married 'her young man' in February 1952. She never was awarded her hospital badge. She and her husband rented a flat above a shop and she worked as a staff nurse at a local geriatric hospital to keep them both alive whilst his business built up and more cars filled the roads.

And Margery Harvey, the nervous young woman who had hesitated outside Albert Terrace in what seemed a lifetime ago. She also undertook midwifery training and qualified, but decided midwifery was not for her. Too limited. The three 'B's' she called it. Babies, bottoms and bosoms. Never having lost the itch to know more she applied to the local authority for sponsorship and did a full time university course in public health and preventative medicine. She became a Health Visitor. But that is another story. . .

j